COMPUTER PROJECTS
FOR RAILWAY MODELLERS

COMPUTER PROJECTS
FOR RAILWAY
MODELLERS

With
program listings
for Sinclair ZX Spectrum
and BBC Microcomputer (Model B)

ROGER AMOS & MARTIN COCK

Patrick Stephens
Wellingborough, Northamptonshire

First published in 1987

British Library Cataloguing in Publication Data

Amos, Roger
   Computer projects for railway modellers.
   1. Railroads—Models—Data processing
   2. Microcomputers
   I. Title
   625.1'9'0285416   TF197

   ISBN 0-85059-796-X

*Patrick Stephens Limited is part of the
Thorsons Publishing Group*

Printed and bound in Great Britain by
Whitstable Litho Ltd., Whitstable, Kent.

The abbreviation 'BBC Micro' or 'BBC' has been
used throughout this book for the British
Broadcasting Corporation Microcomputer System.

Neither the authors nor the publisher can be held
responsible for damage to computers or other
equipment arising out of the use or adaptation of
projects described in this book.

Contents

Introduction

Home computer users and railway modellers have much in common. Both pastimes have, with some justification, been described as 'father-and-son' hobbies. Both, if indulged beyond the levels of just playing ready-bought games or of running the train set on the lounge floor, can become demanding in terms of time, space and intellectual resources. And both can be tremendously rewarding.

Both hobbies are subject to the same vicissitudes of the market. Recent years have seen the takeover of Airfix by Mainline and then that of Mainline by Dapol; so too Sinclair was taken over by Amstrad and it was perhaps not insignificant that in the 1986 *Which Computer?* show such household names as Acorn, Sinclair and Tatung were conspicuous by their absence. And yet the model shops assure us that at the time of writing (autumn 1986) they could sell model railway equipment faster than they can receive stocks. And shortly before Christmas 1985 attempts to purchase a disc drive for the BBC revealed that every major supplier had waiting lists.

Another point of contact between the two hobbies is that they are both applications of electronics. Computers plainly are — only slowly have the traditional model railway equipment manufacturers capitalized on the multifarious ways in which electronics can improve model railway operation but the two books *Practical Electronics for Railway Modellers* and *Practical Electronics for Railway Modellers 2* by Roger Amos (Patrick Stephens Ltd, 1982 and 1985) created and continue to create a lot of interest in the application of electronics to the day-to-day running of model railways. The second book in particular introduced railway modellers to the world of digital electronics. Home computers are simply the natural extension of that technology. They could be defined as 'general purpose logic circuits'. For the same machine is capable of being a calculator, an arcade game, a word processor, a model railway controller, signalbox or sound effects unit depending on the set of instructions, the *program*, that we give it.

This book is intended primarily for the railway modeller who has or who intends to get a home computer and who wonders if he can make use of his computer on his model railway and, if so, how. It falls into two main sections: (i) projects in which the computer is not electrically connected to the railway; and (ii) projects in which an electrical connection, and therefore an interface of some kind, is used. Some previous knowledge of electronics is essential for a full appreciation of this latter section of the book. That knowledge may be gained from the two previously mentioned books. A useful set of appendices provides a wealth of background information.

One of the biggest problems confronting the authors of this book was the same as that which confronts the intending home computer buyer — which computer to use? When work began on this book three machines dominated the UK home computer market: (i) the BBC Micro (Model B) from Acorn; (ii) the Sinclair ZX Spectrum; and (iii) the Commodore 64. To this list could have been added the Acorn Electron, essentially a simplified version of the BBC. Subsequently other machines have gained in popularity such as the Sinclair QL and several machines from Amstrad.

Even to have triplicated the projects so that versions were included for each of the original three would have led to a very ungainly book. Moreover, it is not possible to compile simply a set of program listings for modellers to key in and use immediately on their layouts since every layout is different and every modeller wants different facilities. So the listings given in this book are best regarded as 'examples' showing the way in which the authors set about creating the desired effects. No claim is made that they are the most elegant means to achieve the end, but they are known to work. It is understood, however, that the reader will in all probability need to 'customize' the listing to suit his individual requirements.

A compromise was reached over the choice of machines. The BBC Micro has long been a favourite of electronics dabblers because of its comprehensive built-in interfaces and very versatile BASIC. Also as this machine is widely used in schools and colleges it is likely to be familiar to many readers even if they don't own one. Furthermore programs in BBC BASIC can often also be run on the

Acorn Electron and Tatung Einstein (though the authors have not tested this). So the BBC was chosen as the mainstay of the book. The Sinclair Spectrum was also used because its remarkably low price has made it the top-selling home computer in the UK and it has been the means by which many have gained their first experience of microcomputers. In some respects, eg its very limited BASIC, it is the exact opposite of the BBC Micro. So by embracing the BBC Micro and the Spectrum the field has been bracketed. Commodore 64 owners, for instance, confronted with a BBC BASIC listing and a Spectrum BASIC listing, should — with the aid of their machine's user guide — be able to deduce how to implement the application on their own machines. Incidentally the present authors gratefully acknowledge the help given by Dr John Down in the form of interface designs for the Spectrum: his work forms the basis of chapters 7 and 8 of this book.

What level of computing experience is assumed of readers? The answer is a little. Every program but one of those described in this book is in BASIC throughout — the one exception is partially in 6502 Assembly Language, which is available as a 'language within a language' on the BBC Micro and Acorn Electron. It is not the place of this book to be a complete course in BASIC. Most home computers are supplied with some kind of guide to BASIC and there are, anyway, plenty of excellent BASIC tutors available from bookshops, computer dealers and libraries. Appendix 2 gives a potted guide to the internal workings of microcomputers and should, we hope, help the beginner to understand something of what actually goes on inside his machine.

There are those who argue that there is no place for computers on model railways. They enjoy driving their trains and feel much the same threat from the new technology as a traditional craftsman must feel when told that his workshop is to be automated. To such modellers we say this — we too enjoy driving our trains and would hastily pull the plug out if there was any suggestion that the computer was going to spoil our enjoyment of our hobby. The computer is meant to be man's servant, taking over the thankless menial jobs, leaving man free to get on with more important — and enjoyable — activities.

Undoubtedly a program could be written to allow a computer to take over and run a whole layout, driving the trains, switching the turnouts etc. Combining several of the programs in this book would enable you to do just that — and then you could sit back and leave the computer to get on with it if you wished. A more likely scenario is this — if your (or your club's) layout normally demands four operators and only one or two are available, you can let the computer play the parts of the absent operators, so the operating session isn't lost. You drive your trains in the time-honoured traditional manner — and you will be passing trains going the other way, coming up behind the late-running local in front and so on, just as if the other operators were all present. Or the computer can look after the layout management — switching controllers between control zones — leaving you to get on with the train driving that you enjoy.

Has this whetted your appetite? Then read on!

Glossary of computer terms

Analogue Storage or representation of variable quantities in a means which is infinitely variable, eg, the representation of time by the hands of a conventional clock or watch. Quantities in analogue form must be converted to digital form before they can be processed by a computer. The BBC Micro contains four built-in analogue-to-digital converters; such devices for the Spectrum must be bought as add-ons.

ASCII (American Standard Code for Information Interchange). A code whereby a complete set of alphanumerical characters, punctuation marks, other symbols and control codes is represented by 7-bit numbers, ie, numbers between 0 and 127. ASCII is used with varying degrees of adaptation by most home computers including the BBC Micro and the Spectrum.

Assembler, assembly language A program which generates (assembles) machine code from simple mnemonic instructions representing the microprocessor's operations. A program made up of such mnemonic instructions is said to be in assembly language.

BASIC (Beginners' All-purpose Symbolic Instruction Code.) The language that is most commonly used in home computers because of its simple English-like keywords and structure and its clear system of error messages.

Binary notation A system for the representation of numbers using only the digits '1' and '0'. In computers and other digital equipment the two states '1' and '0' are represented by high and low voltages.

Bit (Abbreviation of binary digit.) The smallest unit of data, a single '1' or '0'.

Bus A common data or address line whereby data are transmitted around the computer. Access to the computer's busses normally makes it possible for additional interfaces to be connected to it.

Byte The smallest unit of memory that a microprocesser can access — the Z80 and 6502 microprocessors used in the Spectrum and BBC Micro are 8-bit microprocessors, so each byte in these machines consists of 8 bits. This allows 2^8 = 256 possibilities, so each byte can be considered as a whole number between 0 (binary 00000000) and 255 (binary 11111111). It is not possible on a microcomputer to address individual *bits*. To access a bit it is necessary to perform a manipulation on the whole byte. Thus on the BBC Micro to set bit 7 of memory location &3000 you would need to proceed as follows: (BASIC ?&3000 = ?&3000 OR 128; Assembler LDA&3000: ORA 128:STA&3000)

Central processing unit The heart of a computer where the actual arithmetical and logical operations on data take place. In a microcomputer this is a single integrated circuit called the microprocessor.

Data (Plural of *datum*.) A collective term for the units of information which a computer processes. Such data are generally in digital form; if in analogue form they must be converted to digital before further processing.

Digital Representation or storage of quantities as whole numbers of units which inside the computer are in binary format.

Filing system A means whereby programs and data can be stored for future use. The filing systems in most common use on home computers are cassette tape, floppy disc and floppy tape (micro-drive).

Hexadecimal A number notation system using 16 different symbols instead of the decimal system (using 10) with which we are most familiar. The symbols 0 to 9 are retained and supplemented by A to F representing the decimal numbes 10 to 15. Familiarity with the hexadecimal system is useful since all addresses in the 64 kbyte memory map common to 8-bit microcomputers can be conveniently represented as four-digit numbers from &0000 to &FFFF. Moreover the BBC Micro's machine operating system only accepts and issues numbers in hexadecimal format. In BBC BASIC hexadecimal inputs are preceded by an ampersand (&) and this convention is widely used in publications for BBC Micro users, including this book. The Spectrum does not normally work in hexadecimal but publications for Spectrum users generally prefix or suffix an 'h' or 'H' to signify hexadecimal notation.

Integer variable In BBC BASIC a variable whose label ends in % and which is only capable of storing whole numbers between −2,147,483,648 and 2,147,483,648.

Integrated circuit An electronic circuit generally containing the equivalent of many transistors and other components on a single piece ('chip') of silicon.

Interface An electronic circuit which connects a microcomputer to other electronic/electrical equipment.

Kilobyte A measurement of memory storage capacity equivalent to 1024 ($=2^{10}$) bytes. Often written 'kbyte'.

Language A program used to make communication with the computer more convenient. For instance, commonly used routines are typically accessed by the entry of a single descriptive keyword. Computer languages are divided into *low-level* languages such as assemblers which have a close relationship to the machine code which the microprocessor actually understands and *high-level* languages such as BASIC, FORTH and PASCAL which bear little resemblance to machine code but are considerably easier for the programmer to handle.

Machine code Instructions in a form which the central processing unit (the microprocessor in a microcomputer) can accept and act upon without need for interpretation or compilation.

Megabyte A measurement of memory storage capacity equivalent to 1024 ($=2^{10}$) kilobytes or 1,048,576 bytes.

Memory That part of the computer which the microprocessor accesses directly to read instructions and data and to store data. Memory is divided into two distinct types, ROM and RAM, *qv*.

Memory map A representation of the way in which a computer organizes its memory. For an 8-bit microcomputer having a 64 kbyte memory map, typically an upright box is drawn with &0000 at the bottom and &FFFF at the top (sometimes the other way round). Different zones are then drawn to show ROM, user RAM and areas of RAM reserved by the machine for workspace etc.

Microcomputer An electronic circuit for data processing consisting of a microprocessor, banks of memory (usually including both RAM and ROM) and interfaces whereby instructions and data can be entered and processed data communicated to the outside world.

Microprocessor A single integrated circuit capable of working through a series of instructions and in response to them performing simple arithmetical and logical operations on numbers.

Operating system Those machine code routines which are essential to a microcomputer's operation irrespective of the current language. They include routines associated with input from the keyboard, output to the monitor, the sound system and loading and saving operations on the filing system.

Peek To read the contents of one specific byte of memory. In Spectrum BASIC, but not BBC BASIC, PEEK is a keyword: the term is nevertheless widely used by BBC users.

Peripheral (1) Any device outside a computer but normally connected to it for its operation, eg, a monitor, printer or disc or tape drive. (2) Within the computer a peripheral is the interface through which the microprocessor communicates with a peripheral as defined in (1).

Poke To insert a byte into a specific memory location. In Spectrum BASIC, but not BBC BASIC, POKE is a keyword: the term is nevertheless widely used by BBC users.

Procedure In BBC BASIC and in PASCAL this is a structure similar to a subroutine (*qv*) but called by name; it also includes facilities whereby parameters (quantities and strings) can be passed to the procedure for processing.

Program A series of instructions through which a computer or microprocessor works.

RAM (Random-Access Memory.) Memory in which the computer stores user-entered programs and data and data generated by the program including the contents of the monitor screen. Most forms of RAM lose their contents when the machine is switched off, hence the necessity to save wanted data or programs on the filing system before switching the machine off.

Read To access data, whether from a memory location (when it means much the same as peek), a filing system or a peripheral.

Reset To make a bit a '0'.

ROM (Read-Only Memory.) A form of memory in which the program or data is fixed and cannot be altered by the computer: the contents of ROM are retained when the computer is switched off. In a home computer the BASIC interpreter and operating system routines are generally resident in ROM.

Set To make a bit a '1'.

Subroutine When a certain routine is required at several different points in a program it is clearly wasteful of programming time and of machine memory to key in those same instructions over and over again. One solution is to include them in a subroutine which can be called whenever needed. In BASIC a subroutine is called with the GOSUB statement (spelt GO SUB in Spectrum BASIC) followed by the line number for the start of the subroutine. The subroutine is terminated by RETURN, whereupon control is returned to the statement immediately after the calling GOSUB.

TTL (Transistor/Transistor Logic.) A series of integrated circuits used for logic functions and widely used as support devices in microcomputers and interfaces.

User port An interface available to the user for the connection of digital equipment to the computer.

Variable In BASIC a label representing a number or a string of characters which may vary. The variable contents are held in RAM at a location which the computer can look up.

Write To send data whether to a memory location (when it means much the same as poke) or to a filing system or to a peripheral.

Chapter 1

Sequential display (timetable) generator

One of the most frequent — and simplest — applications of micro-computers on model railways is the display of information concerning the operations currently in progress. At exhibitions this helps spectators to understand what is going on and so enhances their enjoyment of the layout. Another use is to display a set of instructions for the layout operators as they set up or run the layout. Each display consists of a sequence of 'pages' which is advanced by the operator touching a key.

A typical operation sequence for a layout modelling current practice at Carstairs on British Rail's West Coast Main Line might be:

(Page 1)
11.14 hrs
Manchester-Glasgow/Liverpool-Edinburgh express arrives and is divided

(Page 2)
11.16 hrs
Manchester-Glasgow portion of express departs
Loco coupled to Liverpool-Edinburgh portion

(Page 3)
11.19 hrs
Liverpool-Edinburgh portion departs

This kind of program is quite simple to create. Tables 1.1 and 1.2 show the heart of such a program plus the first three subroutines which display the three movements at Carstairs shown above.

Table 1.1 Sequential display generator (BBC)

```
10 REM SEQUENTIAL DISPLAY GENERATOR
20 REM ROGER S AMOS 20.2.85
30 N%=3:REM N%=NUMBER OF PAGES IN DISPLAY
40 FOR P%=1 TO N%
50   CLS:PRINT P%:GOSUB(P%*100)
60   G%=GET
70   NEXT P%
80 GOTO40
90 END
100 REM START OF PAGE
110 PRINT "11.14 hrs"
120 PRINT
130 PRINT "Manchester-Glasgow/Liverpool-Edinburgh"
140 PRINT"express arrives and is divided"
195 RETURN
200 REM START OF PAGE
210 PRINT "11.16 hrs"
220 PRINT
230 PRINT "Manchester-Glasgow portion of express"
240 PRINT "departs"
250 PRINT "Loco coupled to Liverpool-"
260 PRINT "Edinburgh portion"
295 RETURN
300 REM START OF PAGE
310 PRINT "11.19 hrs"
320 PRINT
330 PRINT "Liverpool-Edinburgh portion departs"
395 RETURN
```

Table 1.2 Sequential display generator (Spectrum)

```
10 REM SEQUENTIAL DISPLAY GENERATOR
20 REM ROGER S AMOS 20.2.85
30 LET n = 3 : REM no of pages in sequence
40 FOR p = 1 TO n
50 CLS : PRINT p : GO SUB(p*100)
60 PAUSE 0
70 NEXT p
80 GO TO 40
90 STOP
100 PRINT
110 PRINT "11.14 hrs"
120 PRINT
130 PRINT "Manchester-Glasgow/Liverpool-"
140 PRINT "Edinburgh express arrives and"
```

```
150 PRINT "is divided"
195 RETURN
200 PRINT
210 PRINT "11.16 hrs"
220 PRINT
230 PRINT "Manchester-Glasgow portion of express departs"
240 PRINT
250 PRINT "Loco coupled to Liverpool-Edinburgh portion"
295 RETURN
300 PRINT
310 PRINT "11.19 hrs"
320 PRINT
330 PRINT "Liverpool-Edinburgh portion departs"
395 RETURN
```

Your first decision must be on the number of 'pages' in your display, since this number is the value given to the variable in line 30 — 3 in our listing. (If you do not know how many pages you will need, it is far preferable to *overprescribe* as we shall see.) The maximum number of pages possible with the program in its present form is one hundredth of the greatest possible line number acceptable to your computer. This gives you the possibility of 650 pages on the BBC/Electron or 99 on the Spectrum. This should be more than adequate for most purposes unless you happen to be modelling Clapham Junction or Birmingham New Street.

The heart of the program is the FOR... TO... NEXT loop in lines 40 to 70. As P% or p works through all the whole numbers from 1 to N% or n, line 50 clears the screen and calls the subroutine which starts at the line whose number equals 100 times P% or p. Only the first three subroutines are shown in the listings given. Each subroutine contains the PRINT instructions to set up a page and each begins — in our program — with its page number. This could be omitted, but in fact is most useful in finding one's way around the sequence.

When the contents of the page have been printed, the program pointer returns to line 60 whereupon the computer waits until any key — or at least any key that generates an ASCII code — is pressed. If you wish to be more specific (perhaps to prevent unauthorized tampering with the sequence) you could replace line 60 with a statement such as:

```
60 REPEAT UNTIL GET = 32 (BBC/Electron)
```

or on the Spectrum:

```
60 LET a$ = INKEY$: IF CODE a$ = 32 THEN GO TO 70
65 GO TO 60
```

which would require the space bar to be pressed. The action could
be made specific for any key by choosing a different ASCII code.

Line 80 is optional. If included it will cause the sequence to begin
again after the last page has been displayed. If omitted, the
program will simply finish after the last page, the computer
returning to the command mode.

The subroutines start at line 100. Note that the first line of each
subroutine will have a line number which is a multiple of 100 and
each line is identical. Similarly the last line of each subroutine (each
line whose number ends in 95) is identical. This means that on the
BBC you can generate these particular lines very rapidly by typing
in the following two lines:

```
*KEY9 PRINT P%:REM START OF PAGE!M
AUTO 100,100
```

Now simply hold function key 9 down and watch the lines being
generated until you reach the required 100 times N%. In the same
way you can set up another key (or the same one) to generate all
the 'RETURN' lines:

```
*KEY8 RETURN!M
AUTO 195,100
```

Having generated the first and last lines of the requisite number of
subroutines, all that is needed is to enter the required PRINT
instructions on intervening lines, as exemplified in the three
subroutines in the listings given.

Suppose, however, that you are developing an exhibition
sequence but do not yet know exactly how many operations will be
involved and therefore the number of pages required. You may
want to add or delete pages. One way to cater for this is as follows.
Deliberately choose a value of N% (or n) rather greater than you
think you will need. For example, if you guess you will need 20, set
N% at 100. Now amend the main program by typing in the following additional lines:

(For the BBC/Electron)

```
45 Z%=FALSE
55 IF Z% GOTO 70
```

(For the Spectrum)

```
45 LET z=0
55 IF z THEN GO TO 70
```

Now put into each subroutine (eg on lines whose numbers end in 05) a line such as this:

(For the BBC/Electron)

```
105 Z%=TRUE
```

(For the Spectrum)

```
105 LET z=255
```

BBC users could of course use a function key and AUTO command to generate these lines. Now choose 20 *well spaced* subroutines, eg, those beginning on lines 300, 800, 1300, 1800, 2300, 2800, 3300, 3800, 4300, 4800, 5300, 5800, 6300, 6800, 7300, 7800, 8300 and 8800, and put your PRINT instructions into these. Also in these and *only* in these *delete* the line saying Z%=TRUE or LET z=255.

The program will now run as though it contains only those 20 subroutines that you have used; the others, which make Z%=TRUE or z=255, will be skipped. (Actually, they aren't skipped — they are executed, even though they are blank but for the page number. It is line 60 which is skipped, so that instead of waiting for a key to be pressed the computer goes straight on to the next page. It only pauses at the 'used' pages from which the Z%=TRUE or LET z=255 statement has been deleted.) The only evidence that all is not as simple as it seems will be a slight hesitation between pages and the fact that the page numbers will not be consecutive.

You can now cater for new operations by bringing empty pages into the sequence at any time. Simply write in suitable PRINT statements and delete the Z%=TRUE (z=255) statements. Unwanted pages can be removed by incorporating a Z%=TRUE (or z=255) statement.

A useful facility while experimenting with this kind of program is that you can call up the subroutine for any page from the immediate mode by simply typing in GOSUB *n* [RETURN], where *n* is 100 times the required page number. But a word of warning: because this program uses calculated line numbers, you *cannot* RENUMBER (BBC/Electron) it.

It is also possible to link 'timetable' information of the kind displayed by this program with a clock program so that the pages are advanced automatically at certain times. We shall see how to do this in the next chapter.

Chapter 2

Variable-speed clock

Many modellers delight in emulating prototype practice by operating to a timetable, especially on exhibition layouts. But there is a difficulty. Even the busiest prototype lines have their quiet spells — it is easily possible to spend thirty minutes on a Saturday or Sunday afternoon beside the West Coast Main Line at Rugby and see no moving trains at all. Visitors to exhibitions, however, do not spend their money to watch model railways where nothing happens for long periods, no matter how prototypical.

To overcome this, many modellers employ an accelerated clock. That is, the timetable is governed by a clock running at several times normal speed. The late Rev Teddy Boston's layout 'Olton Priors', based on GWR practice, uses a conventional mechanical clock whose escapement was modified so that it runs at eight times normal speed. This enables a 24-hour timetable to be compressed into a workable three-hour session.

If you are a competent mechanic — and of course many railway modellers are — you may be able to carry out a similar modification. Alternatively, an accelerated electronic digital clock would be quite easy to make. But a microcomputer contains all the electronics needed to provide a clock capable of running at virtually any speed and of offering a number of useful ancillary features. Table 2.1 gives a suitable program listing for the BBC/Electron and Table 2.2 one for the Spectrum.

Table 2.1 Variable speed clock (BBC)

```
10 REM VARIABLE SPEED CLOCK
20 REM ROGER S. AMOS 21.1.85
30 MODE6:PRINTTAB(11,3);"VARIABLE SPEED CLOCK"
40 INPUT '"Enter acceleration factor    "F
```

```
 50  PRINT'"Enter starting time:"
 60  INPUT'"Hours    "H%
 70  INPUT'"Minutes "M%
 80  PRINT'"Press SPACE BAR to start clock"
 90  REPEATUNTILGET=32
100  CLS:TIME=0
110  VDU23;8202;0;0;0;
120  PRINTTAB(7,1);"TIME NOW:    :"
130  REPEAT
140    N%=INT(M%+(TIME*F)/6000)
150    O%=N%MOD60:I%=(N%DIV60)+H%
160    IF O%<10 THEN PRINTTAB(20,1);0;O%:ELSEPRINTTAB(20,1);
O%
170    I%=I%MOD24
180    IF I%<10 THEN PRINTTAB(17,1);0;I%:ELSEPRINTTAB(17,1);
I%
190    IFINKEY(-82)THEN T=TIME:REPEATUNTILINKEY(-84):TIME=T
200    IF I%=6 AND O%=45 PROCmilktrain
210    IF I%=6 AND O%=50 PROCclear
220    IF I%=6 AND O%=55 PROClocal
230    IF I%=7 AND O%=0 PROCclear
240    UNTIL0
250  END
260  DEFPROCmilktrain
270  PRINTTAB(0,5);"Milk train arrives from Churminster
Newton"
280  ENDPROC
290  DEFPROClocal
300  PRINTTAB(0,5);"Local train leaves for Churchward"
310  ENDPROC
320  DEFPROCclear:PRINTTAB(0,5);SPC(120):ENDPROC
```

Table 2.2 Variable speed clock (Spectrum)

```
 10  REM VARIABLE SPEED CLOCK
 20  REM ROGER S. AMOS 23.3.85
 30  CLS :PRINT AT 2,5; "VARIABLE SPEED CLOCK"
 40  INPUT "Enter acceleration factor    ";f
 50  PRINT "Enter starting time:"
 60  INPUT "Hours    ";hrs
 70  INPUT "Minutes ";min
 75  PRINT
 80  PRINT "Press space bar to start clock"
 90  LET a$ = INKEY$: IF CODE a$ = 32 THEN GO TO 100
 95  GO TO 90
100  CLS: FOR m = 23672 TO 23674 : POKE m,0 : NEXT m
120  PRINT AT 1,7; "TIME NOW:    :"
130  LET time = (PEEK 23672+256*PEEK 23673+65536*PEEK 23674)
140  LET n = INT(min+(time*f)/3000)
```

```
  150 LET o = (n/60)-INT(n/60): LET o = INT(60*o): LET i = IN
T (n/60)+hrs
  160 IF o<10 THEN PRINT AT 1,17;0;o
  165 IF o>=10 THEN PRINT AT 1,17;o
  170 IF i<24 THEN GO TO 180
  175 LET i = i-24 : GO TO 170
  180 IF i<10 THEN PRINT AT 1,17;0;i
  185 IF i>=10 THEN PRINT AT 1,17;i
  190 LET a$ = INKEY$: IF a$ = "s" OR a$ = "S" THEN LET a = P
EEK 23672 : LET b = PEEK 23673 : LET c = PEEK 23674 : PAUSE 0
 : POKE 23672,a : POKE 23673,b : POKE 23674,c
  200 IF i=6 AND o=45 THEN GO SUB 260
  210 IF i=6 AND o=50 THEN GO SUB 320
  220 IF i=6 AND o=55 THEN GO SUB 290
  230 IF i=7 AND o=0 THEN GO SUB 320
  240 GO TO 130
  260 PRINT AT 5,0; "Milk train arrives from": PRINT "Churmin
ster Newton": RETURN
  290 PRINT AT 5,0; "Local train leaves for": PRINT "Churchwa
rd": RETURN
  320 PRINT AT 5,0; " ";: FOR x = 1 TO 119: PRINT " ";: NEXT
x: RETURN
```

Mode 6 in line 30 (BBC only) is arbitrary — any screen mode could be used, although in 20-column modes some repositioning of characters on the screen will be needed.

In line 40 the acceleration factor is put into the real variable F (f in the Spectrum). Using a real variable rather than an integer variable makes it possible to use fractional factors such as 7.5 or 3.1416 if you wish to. (Of course, if you enter 1 the clock will run at normal speed and if you enter numbers less than 1 such as 0.5 or 0.33 the clock will run slower than normal.)

Lines 50 to 70 allow the user to enter any desired starting time. So if you are running a 24-hour timetable with an acceleration factor of 6 and the first movement scheduled for 06.00 hrs, you don't have to wait a full one hour to begin! Lines 80 to 95 allow the clock to be started displaying any suitable time whenever convenient at the touch of the space bar.

Lines 100 to 130 set up the clock by clearing the screen, turning off the cursor (BBC only) and poking 0 into the bytes of memory concerned with internal timekeeping. These are incremented at 10 ms intervals on the BBC and 20 ms intervals on the Spectrum. The words 'TIME NOW: :' are printed on the screen in readiness for the clock display itself.

The main body of the program is contained in the loop from line

130 to line 240. In line 140 the current time reading is multiplied by the acceleration factor and divided by 6000 on the BBC (3000 on the Spectrum) to convert it to minutes. To this is added the number of minutes in the starting time, the resultant number being stored in the variable N% (n in the Spectrum). Line 150 performs integer division by 60 on N% (or n), the dividend plus the number of hours in the starting time giving the number of hours in I% (i) and the modulus the number of minutes in O% (o).

Lines 160 and 165 print the number of minutes, inserting a 0 before the number if less than 10. Lines 170 and 175 enable the clock to run indefinitely by resetting the number of hours to 0 each time it reaches 24. If you want a 12-hour rather than a 24-hour clock, amend the references to 24 in these lines to 12. Lines 180 and 185 print the number of hours, inserting a 0 before the number if less than 10.

Line 190 gives a useful facility. If you should experience 'operating difficulties' (to use prototype railway jargon) you may stop the clock, storing the current internal time in the variable T (the variables a, b and c in the Spectrum) and restart it when the problems are sorted out, poking the stored values back into the internal clock. To stop the clock press 'S' (for STOP). To restart it press 'G' (for GO) — on the Spectrum press any key to restart. Stopping the clock is a luxury in which we modellers have a considerable advantage over British Rail!

Lines 200 to 230 and 260 to 320 are optional and for example only. They show how the clock program can be used to drive a sequential display like that described in the previous chapter, but this time under automatic timed control. The BBC version of the program uses procedures rather than subroutines; these resemble subroutines but are called by name rather than line number. PROCclear or the subroutine at line 320 is used to clear the currently displayed message after five scale minutes of display by printing three (four in the Spectrum) lines of spaces over it. This is preferable to the use of a CLS statement, since that would clear the whole screen including the clock display. (We could regenerate the clock display by incorporating line 120 into the loop, but this results in a display that flickers in a rather distracting manner.)

As many procedures or subroutines as you wish can be called by time-conditional statements of the kind seen in lines 200 to 230, but as more are incorporated into the loop, so the loop takes longer to execute. Since, however, the displayed time is based on the computer's own internal clock whose timekeeping is independent of the program being executed, at each pass of the loop the updated time will be consistently accurate.

Chapter 3

Sound effects generator (BBC Micro only)

Some popular micros which incorporate the 76489 or similar complex sound generator ICS are capable of producing a wide variety of sounds under the control of BASIC. In this category are the BBC Micro, Commodore 64 and Tatung Einstein. This chapter describes a fairly simple program for the BBC Micro which may be adaptable for similarly equipped machines. Unfortunately the Sinclair Spectrum and Acorn Electron are rather limited in their internal sound capabilities although separate sound effects units might make it possible for these machines to run this kind of program.

Unlike the projects described in the two previous chapters which unquestionably perform the task for which they are intended, the success of this program is a subjective judgement. You may consider the sounds lifelike or you may reckon that they are a very poor approximation of the real thing. Even an ic like the 76489 has its limitations — when all is said and done it is *not* a steam locomotive, nor a diesel. And any attempt to reproduce even the most authentic recording of a *Castle* or a *Peak* through the tiny speaker of a BBC Micro is likely to lead to disappointing results. Our answer to any who criticise the realism of the sounds produced by this program is that we make no claim that this is the 'last word' in sound effects, the range of sounds possible from the BBC Micro must approach infinity (using the ENVELOPE facility) and that if you can improve on this, the field is open to you to do so. Nevertheless many who have heard this program in use have been impressed by its 'atmospheric' sound effects. Young children, in particular, find it absolutely fascinating.

Five types of train are simulated to suit a range of tastes. A steam loco effect gives variable chuff rate based on a 6-foot driving wheel diameter. At rest the loco just hisses gently. At speeds from 1 mph to 9 mph both chuff rate *and* duration are linked to speed. Above 9 mph chuff duration is fixed but frequency is proportional to speed. A diesel loco and a diesel multiple unit (DMU) sound are included. These both pose considerable problems of simulation, because their sounds are not proportional to speed. An electric locomotive and an electric multiple unit sound are easier, being again proportional to speed.

In all five options speed is controlled by the ⭡ (up cursor) and ⭣ (down cursor) keys and is displayed on the screen. Top speed is 127 mph. The 'W' key is the whistle/horn lever. On the steam option this is a simulated steam whistle with realistic rise, decay and 'wobble' together with the hiss of escaping steam. The steam whistle continues to sound as long as the 'W' key is held down. Unfortunately the steam whistle silences the chuffs — we could find no way to keep both sounding together. On the diesel and electric options the whistle is a two-tone horn. This sounds the low note for as long as the key is depressed — when the key is released the high note is sounded for the same period as the low note. On all options the 'B' button sounds the automatic warning system (AWS) bell and the 'H' button the AWS horn. Those who have travelled in train cabs (or in the front seat of a DMU) will know that the bell sounds automatically on approaching a clear (green) signal and the horn sounds when approaching a signal at danger or caution.

Lines 20 and 30 set up the two ENVELOPEs used by the program. ENVELOPEs provide a means whereby the attack, decay, sustain and release phases of a sound can be controlled more precisely than by the SOUND statement on its own. Up to 16 ENVELOPEs can be used in the BBC, giving ample scope to those who wish to refine this program, but we found that ENVELOPE1 (line 20) gave a rapidly decaying sound ideal for the AWS bell, the rapid chuffs of a steam loco at speed and the 'clatter' of a well-worn diesel engine, while ENVELOPE2 (line 30) gives a gentler decay for the AWS horn.

Line 40 initials certain variables to ensure that, for example, on entry to the program speed (held in S%) is nil and the whistle (W%) is off. Line 50 tells the computer that on error conditions — and pressing the ESCAPE key generates an error — the computer is to return to the main menu (at line 70). Line 60 disables cursor editing — we want to use the cursor keys for speed control and we don't want to have to read and write cursors wandering up and down the screen.

The menu is defined in lines 70 to 90 and in the data in line 660. Although MODE6 is specified in line 70, any MODE could be used. Line 90 provides a convenient means of selecting routines from a menu, the final ELSE statement trapping any entries outside of the legal range.

Lines 100 to 510 incorporate the routines selected from the menu, the last ('Quit program') re-enabling the cursor editing (line 500). Each of the five 'train' routines is essentially similar in structure, a GOTO loop beginning with PROCSPEED: all the PROCedures are defined at the end of the program.

PROCSPEED tests if the cursor keys are being pressed and increases or decreases the speed (and its display) accordingly. In fact the speed contained in S% can be between 0 and 255, but the displayed speed is divided by 2, 127 being a more credible top speed. The choice of 255, however, enables the speed to be stored in one byte if perhaps the program is linked via the user port to a controller (see, for instance, Chapters 6 and 8). PROCSPEED also tests the 'B' and 'H' keys and, if these are pressed, calls the bell and horn routines, PROCBELL and PROCHORN.

This next step in each loop is the whistle option. This is covered by lines 120 to 150 in the steam option and by PROCTWOTONE in the other options. All use W% to control the sounding of the whistle.

The remainder of each loop is concerned with the generation of the train sound itself, based on train speed. That for the steam locomotive is most complex, since quite different routines are used for three speed ranges. Below 1 mph the train is assumed to be stationary and only a steady hiss is produced (line 160). Between 1 and 9 mph each long chuff is composed of separate 'units' of white noise of decreasing amplitude (lines 180 to 200) to allow the ATC bell and horn time in which to function. Above 9 mph each chuff becomes a self-contained unit of sound controlled by envelope 1 (line 220).

How the program is used is obviously a matter of individual preference. The computer could be used as a stand-alone sound effects box with an operator using the cursor keys to match the computer's indicated speed to that of the train. If the internal loudspeaker is not adequate it should be possible to use an alternative speaker or an external amplifer to give reproduction of higher quality. Alternatively the BBC's analogue-to-digital converter could be used to allow the computer to sample the output voltage (or control voltage) from a controller (throttle) and determine the speed from this (see Chapter 6). A further alternative is to use the computer itself as a control unit and to download the speed set using the cursor keys to a digital-to-analogue converter for amplification and use as the train's power source. These subjects involve the use of *interfaces* and will be covered in Chapter 8.

3;1 Railway sound effects generator (BBC)

```
10 REM SOUND EFFECTS FOR MODEL RAILWAYS
20 ENVELOPE1,1,0,0,0,3,3,3,40,-10,-10,-10,120,80
30 ENVELOPE2,1,0,0,0,3,3,3,40,0,-40,-10,120,0
40 A=-15:W%=0:S%=0
50 ON ERROR GOTO 70
60 *FX4,1
70 MODE6:VDU23;8202;0;0;0;:PRINT''" MODEL RAILWAY SOUND EF
FECTS GENERATOR":PRINT'SPC(18);"MENU"
80 FORI%=1TO6:PRINT'TAB(0);I%;". ";:READW$:PRINTW$:NEXT:RE
STORE:PRINT''"PLEASE MAKE YOUR CHOICE":PRINT'"Press ESCAPE to
 return to menu"
90 J%=VAL(GET$):ONJ%GOTO100,240,290,340,430,500ELSE90
100 CLS:PRINT''SPC(14);"STEAM SOUNDS"
110 PROCSPEED
120 IFINKEY(-34)W%=W%-5:GOTO140
130 IFW%THENW%=W%+3:ELSEGOTO160
140 IFW%<-15THENW%=-15:ELSEIFW%>0THENW%=0
150 SOUND3,W%,120+ABS(W%)+RND(3),2:SOUND0,-3,4,2:GOTO230
160 IFS%<1SOUND0,-2,4,1:GOTO230
170 IFS%>20GOTO220
180 IFL%<1THENL%=65DIVS%:Z%=Z%+1:A=-15
190 L%=L%-1:IFZ%AND1THENSOUND0,A,5,1:A=A+0.5:ELSESOUND0,0,0
,1
200 IF A>0 THEN A=0
210 GOTO110
220 SOUND&0010,1,5,3:T=TIME:REPEATUNTILTIME-T=(512DIVS%)
230 GOTO110
240 CLS:PRINT''SPC(14);"DIESEL SOUNDS"
250 PROCSPEED
260 PROCTWOTONE
270 FORZ%=1TO3:SOUND&0010,1,5,3:NEXT:SOUND&0010,-3,5,(S%AND
7)+1
280 GOTO250
290 CLS:PRINT''SPC(14);"D.M.U. SOUNDS"
300 PROCSPEED
310 PROCTWOTONE
320 FORZ%=1TO4:SOUND&0010,1,5,3:NEXT:SOUND&0010,-3,5,10-((S
%MOD50)DIV5)
330 GOTO300
```

```
 340 CLS:PRINT''SPC(7);"ELECTRIC LOCOMOTIVE SOUNDS"
 350 PROCSPEED
 360 PROCTWOTONE
 370 IFS%=0THENP%=127:A%=-3:GOTO400
 380 IFS%>0THENP%=P%+1:A%=A%-1:IFP%>143THENP%=143:ELSEIFA%<
-12THENA%=-12
 390 IFS%<0THENP%=P%-1:A%=A%+1:IFP%<127THENP%=127:ELSEIFA%>
-3THENA%=-3
 400 SOUND2,A%,P%,1:SOUND0,A%DIV3,6,1
 410 O%=S%
 420 GOTO350
 430 CLS:PRINT''SPC(14);"E.M.U. SOUNDS"
 440 PROCSPEED
 450 PROCTWOTONE
 460 IFS%>0THENA%=-9:ELSEIFS%=0THENA%=-6:ELSEA%=-3
 470 IFS%THENSOUND2,A%,S%DIV2,1:ELSESOUND2,-3,0,1
 480 O%=S%
 490 GOTO440
 500 *FX4,0
 510 END
 520 DEFPROCBELL:SOUND&0011,1,200,1:ENDPROC
 530 DEFPROCHORN:SOUND1,2,10,1:ENDPROC
 540 DEFPROCSPEED
 550 IFINKEY(-58)THENS%=S%+1:IFS%>255THENS%=255
 560 IFINKEY(-42)THENS%=S%-1:IFS%<0THENS%=0
 570 PRINTTAB(10,10);"SPEED: ";S%DIV2;SPC(4)
 580 IFINKEY(-101)PROCBELL
 590 IFINKEY(-85)PROCHORN
 600 ENDPROC
 610 DEFPROCTWOTONE
 620 IFINKEY(-34)W%=W%+1:P%=37:GOTO640
 630 IFW%THENW%=W%-1:P%=53:IFW%<0THENW%=0
 640 IFW%THENSOUND3,-15,P%,2
 650 ENDPROC
 660 DATA Steam sound, Diesel loco sound, Diesel multiple un
it sound, Electric loco sound, Electric multiple unit sound,
Quit program
```

Interfacing projects

Introduction

The projects described so far in this book have used the computer on its own, ie, without any electrical connection to the model railway. Any data needed by the computer as it runs those programs have to be fed in at the keyboard by the operator.

This section deals with projects in which the computer is connected directly to the model railway or, at least, to electronic circuits intimately involved in the operation of the model railway, such as controllers (throttles) or train detection systems. Thus the computer is able to receive data direct from the layout or to send data to it or both. Data received from the layout might perhaps concern the speed or direction or location of trains. Data sent to the layout could perhaps be a message to stop a certain train as it is in danger of colliding with another.

There are two factors that you must consider before you can undertake any of the projects in this section. Firstly you must have electronic equipment on your layout which is capable of trans-mitting or receiving the necessary data. For instance, you cannot implement the layout mimic diagram (Chapter 4) unless your layout is fitted with suitable train detectors, such as track circuits, which deliver a digital 'yes' or 'no' regarding the occupancy of sections of the layout. Similarly in the progressive cab control project (Chapter 5) the controllers used must be equipped with a digital output indicating whether forward or reverse movement is selected. Although suitable ready-made equipment may be available commercially, it is more likely that you will have to make it yourself or get an electronically minded friend to do so. Circuit diagrams for suitable items are included in Appendix 1 of this book and more detailed accounts are given in *Practical Electronics for Railway Modellers 2* by Roger Amos (Patrick Stephens Ltd, 1985). Some knowledge of electronics is therefore essential and will be assumed throughout this section. Readers having no prior knowledge of the subject are recommended to read the earlier book, *Practical Electronics for Railway Modellers* by Roger Amos (Patrick Stephens Ltd, 1982) and especially the theoretical and practical appendices at the end of the book.

Secondly, even if your *layout* has the necessary electronic access, your *computer* may not have. A facility which allows a computer to receive data from or transmit data to the outside world is called an *interface*. All home computers have at least three interfaces — a keyboard so the user can enter instructions and data, a UHF output which enables the computer to display data on a television screen and a cassette interface so that programs and data can be stored on tape. More sophisticated machines have additional interfaces such as disc and printer interfaces.

The two computers considered in this book, the BBC model B and the ZX Spectrum, could not be further apart in terms of their built-in interfaces. The Spectrum has only the statutory keyboard and cassette interfaces, plus access to its internal busses (more on these later) which enable further interfaces to be added. The BBC of course has these too and also an enviable range of other interfaces — parallel and serial printer, analogue inputs, digital control (user) port, colour monitor and optional disc and speech interfaces. We shall be concerned only with the BBC's analogue and digital control ports. But before Spectrum users give up in disgust, consider that many add-on interfaces are available commercially for the Spectrum and Chapter 7 gives details of a high-quality unit that you can construct (or get made up for you). It should be possible to implement all the following projects on a Spectrum fitted with such an interface.

Despite the BBC's ample provision it is still very easy to run out of interface channels. The mimic diagram, for instance, as described in Chapter 4 can only handle up to 8 sections, there being only eight available bits on the user port. But with the addition of extra electronic circuitry described in Chapter 5 the user port can be extended to provide inputs from up to 128 sections — or even more. But again you will need to build the additional interfacing yourself.

Having established that your computer has a suitable interface, can you connect it straight to, say, your layout's track circuits? Almost certainly yes. Most user ports — certainly that on the BBC Micro — use standard TTL (Transistor/Transistor Logic) which is described in detail in *Practical Electronics for Railway Modellers 2* and which can be connected directly to the model railway equipment described in Appendix 1 of this book.

Interfacing is a particularly exciting and rewarding area of computing. The following chapters show a range of interfacing projects, of varying complexity, and in addition to giving exciting possibilities on your model railway also provide an insight to the internal workings of the microcomputer.

Chapter 4

Layout mimic diagram

Visit a modern signalbox (or tower as they call them in North America) and you cannot fail to be impressed by the huge mimic diagram which tells the signalmen (towermen) all that they need to know about what is happening in the network controlled from the box. Typically the routes are left unilluminated until a train is expected. When the route is set for a train white lights are lit along the tracks cleared for it: as the train enters the area and activates its track circuits the white lights are replaced by red. Prototypical mimic diagrams often display other data such as train reporting numbers and signal aspects.

Your computer can be used fairly easily to produce a simple but highly effective working mimic diagram of your layout. You must have a BBC Micro or Acorn Electron fitted with a user port, although, no doubt, a version of the program could be devised for a Spectrum fitted with a user port (see Chapter 7 for details). The program as described can cope with a layout having up to eight sections. Each section must be monitored by a track circuit or some other train detector delivering a TTL-compatible output (see Appendix 1 for suitable circuits): no other interfacing is necessary. If your layout uses more than eight sections you will need additional interfacing as described in the next chapter. Vacant sections are displayed in green: occupied sections are displayed in red. No other data is displayed by the program as described here, but you are of course free to adapt it in any way you wish.

Software
The program is listed in full in Table 4.1. All that is required to tailor it to your individual layout is the insertion of the number of sections in line 50, the insertion of the name of your layout (or any other legend) in line 560 and the addition of your data to lines 10000 onwards — how to do this is described in detail later.

Mode 2 is used for the display since this makes sixteen colours available. The diagram is drawn in a graphics window while a small text window allows a message to be displayed, eg, the name of the layout.

Each section is assigned its own unique colour in the range 8 to 15, but the video drivers are fooled into thinking initially that all these colours are green (colour 2) using the VDU19 statement (line 5020). The program monitors each section in turn and if the section is occupied changes its colour, again using VDU19, to red (line 640); if it was occupied and has subsequently become vacant once more the section's colour is changed back to green (line 630). VDU19 makes possible very fast colour changes since the computer does not have to redraw each section in its new colour.

Lines 10000 to 10800 are for your section data. PROCsection (lines 5000 to 5150) reads these data and translates them into a screen display. Line 5080 takes the data pointer to a particular section's data statement. Unfortunately this means that you cannot RENUMBER the program or an error will occur.

Mapping your Sections

The BBC's screen is arranged like a piece of graph paper having 1280 × 1024 squares. Each square may be plotted in any colour. In practice this program 'steals' the bottom 150 rows of squares to display messages, so you have an area of 1280 × 874 to play with. It may be helpful in designing the display of your layout to use a piece of graph paper.

Draw your layout using straight lines and marking in your sections. A section may be complex involving main line, sidings and passing loops. A typical section layout is shown in Figure 1. Coordinates are shown for all junctions, bends and endings. You should be able to read these directly off your graph paper.

The first data needed are the coordinates of the point at which the computer begins drawing. In this example point (500,900) is as good as any. All other coordinates required are *relative* to this. A good way of thinking of this process is to consider yourself as having to walk over all the lines and having to count the paces you take, each pace being one square on the screen. If you think of the top of the screen as north, then a move to the west is negative as is one to the south.

Hence, to get to the point (50,900) from point (500,900) requires a move west of 450 and one south of 0, so the required data are (−450,0). Note the minutes sign.

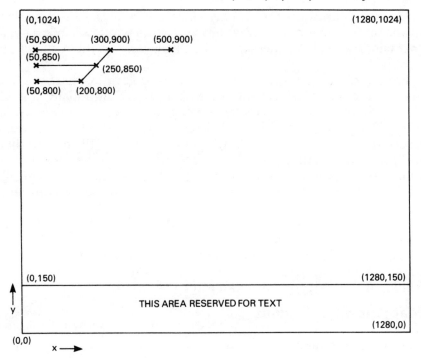

Figure 4.1 *Organization of the screen of the BBC Micro with one section displayed: the co-ordinates are shown for identification only — they are not printed in the display itself.*

Now all you have to do is to 'walk' over the lines until you have covered them all. So from point (50,900) you must go to (300,900), a relative move of (250,0). Then go to (200,800), a relative move of (−100, −100). And so on until your layout is mapped. All of these 'paces' counted need to be strung into the DATA statements in lines 10000 to 10800. Since your tracks will probably be no less than ten squares apart (if they are, you have a very large layout!) the program conveniently multiplies each item of data by 10 to save you from typing in lots of 0s. So all the data you calculated above need dividing by 10. If you are careful you can arrange for most if not all of your coordinates to be multiples of 10. The DATA statement for the section in Figure 1 is:

```
DATA 50,90,-45,0,25,0,-10,-15,0,15,5,5,-20,0,0,0
```

The first two numbers, multiplied by 10, give the starting point. The following seven pairs give the movements needed to draw all the lines. The final two numbers, two 0s, indicate the end of the data for the section. Each data statement must end with two 0s.

The data statements for each section are added into the program at the appropriate line, eg, line 10100 for Section 1, line 10200 for Section 2 and so on up to line 10800 for Section 8. Finally ensure that line 50 includes the number of sections in your layout. So if you have six sections line 50 should read:

```
50 noofsec%=6
```

The REM statement shown in Table 1 is for clarity only and need not be typed in.

Incidentally the system of using relative coordinates for all entries except the first pair allows a section to be drawn elsewhere on the screen by simply changing the first two items of data.

Hardware

Inputs from your track circuits (or other train detectors) are fed directly into the user port connector, one of the row of connectors on the underside of the machine. Further details of the user port will be found in Appendix 3.

The user port inputs are standard TTL pulled up by resistors, so a number of types of drive are possible including outputs from TTL gates (totem-pole or open-collector), the open collectors of discrete npn transistors, relay contacts or opto-isolators. If you opt for the open collectors of discrete transistors ensure that there is no possibility of the collector voltage being pulled above +5V by the base voltage, since this could damage the computer. It is safest to operate the train detection circuitry from a +5V supply.

The program assumes that a logical '0' means 'section occupied'. If your detector uses the opposite convention delete line 610.

Table 1 — Mimic diagram program listing

```
   1 REM *** MIMIC DIAGRAM
   2 REM *** MARTIN J.L. COCK
  10 MODE2
  20 VDU23;8202;0;0;0;
  30 VDU28,0,31,19,28
  40 ?&FE62=0
```

```
   50 noofsec%= :REM YOUR VALUE HERE
  500 FORI%=1 TO noofsec%
  510    PROCsection( I%)
  520    NEXT
  530 VDU24,0;150;1279;1023;
  540 COLOUR132:COLOUR3
  550 CLS
  560 PRINTTAB(2,1);"Your Message Here"
  580 oport%=255
  590 REPEAT
  600    port%=?&FE60
  610    chng%=port% EOR oport%
  620    FOR I%= 0 TO 7
  630       IF 2^I% AND chng% THEN IF 2^I% AND port% THEN
VDU19,I%+8,2,0,0,0
  640       IF 2^I% AND chng% THEN IF 2^I% AND(255-port%) THEN
VDU19,I%+8,1,0,0,0
  650       NEXT
  660    oport%=port%
  670    UNTIL0
 4999 END
 5000 DEFPROCsection(S%)
 5010 LOCAL X%,Y%
 5020 VDU19,(S%+7),2,0,0,0
 5030 GCOL0,(S%+7)
 5080 RESTORE(10000+100*S%)
 5090 READX%,Y%
 5100 MOVEX%*10,Y%*10
 5110 REPEAT
 5120    READX%,Y%
 5130    PLOT1,X%*10,Y%*10
 5140    UNTILX%=0 AND Y%=0
 5150 ENDPROC
10090 REM SECTION 1
10100 REM YOUR DATA HERE
10190 REM SECTION 2
10200 REM YOUR DATA HERE
10290 REM SECTION 3
10300 REM YOUR DATA HERE
10390 REM SECTION 4
10400 REM YOUR DATA HERE
10490 REM SECTION 5
10500 REM YOUR DATA HERE
10590 REM SECTION 6
10600 REM YOUR DATA HERE
10690 REM SECTION 7
10700 REM YOUR DATA HERE
10790 REM SECTION 8
10800 REM YOUR DATA HERE
```

Chapter 5

Progressive cab control (BBC Micro only)

Introduction

Cab control is a system of multiple train management in which the layout is divided into a number of control zones, each of which can be connected by switches to any of several conventional (ie, rheostat or electronic) controllers. As trains proceed from zone to zone the switches are thrown so that each train keeps the same controller (or *cab*) for the whole of its journey. In conventional cab control the switches are thrown manually by the operators — a skilled task recalling that of the old-fashioned signalman (towerman).

In *progressive cab control* (PCC) the principles are the same, but the switching is accomplished automatically leaving the operator(s) free to concentrate on driving the train(s). A TTL-based system was described in *Practical Electronics for Railway Modellers 2*, but even for quite simple layouts that system required complex circuitry.

The trouble with PCC is that inevitably each system must be tailor made for its individual layout and since no two layouts are the same, each PCC system will be unique. The system described in *Practical Electronics for Railway Modellers 2* overcame this to some extent by its modular approach, each system being built up from a number of similar 'modules' whose interconnections could cater for a wide variety of situations. The availability of microcomputers, however, enables us to go a stage further. The computer can handle the *logic* of the system, the software being adapted to take account of the particular demands of the individual layout. Some hardware (an *interface*) is still needed, but rather less than in the system described in *Practical Electronics for Railway Modellers 2*.

Prerequisites

The following are the prerequisites for the PCC system described in

this chapter (in addition to a BBC Micro, interface and software).
Your layout must be divided into a number of control zones by rail
breaks in the live rail. The maximum number of zones is a trade-off
against the number of controllers in use according to the
relationship:

zones = 128/(controllers + 1)

This gives the following combinations of maxima:

42 zones and 2 controllers
32   ''   ''   3   ''
25   ''   ''   4   ''
21   ''   ''   5   ''
18   ''   ''   6   ''
16   ''   ''   7   ''

Seven is the maximum number of controllers.

Each zone must be fitted with a track circuit (or other section
occupation indicator) delivering a TTL-compatible logical '0' when
a train is detected. If a zone contains several track circuits their
outputs may be combined by an AND gate. Each controller should
be fitted with switch or relay contacts which close to give a logical
'0' when *reverse* is selected. Additionally each *significant turnout*
should be fitted with a pair of contacts with action linked to the
turnout setting. By *significant turnout* I mean one at a major junction
whose setting determines which new control zone a train will next
enter. Turnouts into minor sidings or passing loops are not
significant in this sense and need no such contacts.

You can dispense with the latter two requirements if you are
happy to enter controller direction data and significant turnout
setting data at the keyboard. This simplifies and cheapens the
hardware at the cost of extra software and general inconvenience.

Using the user port
The interface connects the BBC's user port. This port offers not
only eight parallel 'bits' (called 'input/output register B' or just
IORB) each of which can be programmed individually as an input
or an output, but also two 'control lines', CB1 and CB2. CB1
provides an interrupt facility which is useful when IORB is
receiving series of bytes from some peripheral device, but is not

relevant in our present application. CB2, however, can be programmed to permit a variety of uses and in our application provides an output to switch the interface between input ('read') and output ('write') modes.

In our application bits 0 to 6 of IORB are permanently configured as outputs and are used as address lines, enabling the computer to address up to 128 independent input and output channels in the interface. Bit 7 of IORB is used for all data input operations. The port is set up for this mode of operation by poking 127 (in binary, 01111111) into the *data direction register*, whose address is &FE62. (BASIC: ?&FE62 = 127. Assembler: LDA#127: STA&FE62.)

The Interface

A circuit diagram of the interface is given in Figure 5.1. How the interface works is really remarkably simple. We'll deal with the data input side first. Bit 7 of IORB (the bit used for data input) is

Figure 5.1 *Interface for progressive cab control: not all the 74LS151s and 74LS138s are shown — unless yours is a very large system not all will be needed.*

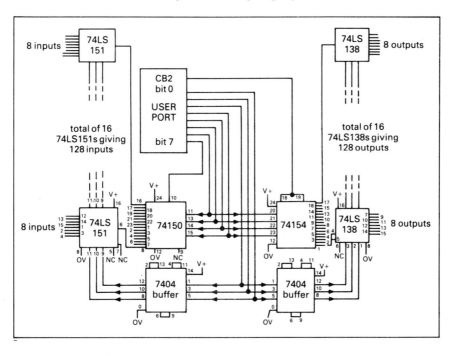

connected straight to the output of a 74150 16-line-to-1-line multiplexer whose address inputs are serviced from IORB bits 3, 4, 5 and 6. The 16 inputs of the 74150 are each fed from the output of a 74LS151 8-line-to-1-line multiplexer, each having its address inputs serviced (via a buffer ICXX) from IORB bits 0, 1 and 2. Each 74LS151 offers 8 inputs giving a total of $16 \times 8 = 128$ independent inputs.

When the computer needs to know the status of one of the 128 inputs, first IORB bits 3 to 6 are set up to address (via the 74150) the appropriate 74LS151 and IORB bits 0 to 2 are set up to point to the appropriate input on the 74LS151. Now the value of IORB is read (as the contents of memory location &FE60) and ANDed with 128 (BASIC: $X = ?$&FE60 AND 128. Assembler: LDA&FE60:AND#128); this will of course yield 128 if bit 7 at the time of reading was a '1', otherwise it will yield a '0'. During all this time the level on CB2 is kept high by keeping the three highest bits of the peripheral control register (&FE6C) as '1's. This maintains the interface in its 'read' mode and prevents the sending out of any unwanted data.

The output side of the interface is almost a mirror image of the input side — indeed Figure 5.1 is drawn to emphasize the symmetry of the unit. Bit 7 of IORB is not used in 'write operations'. CB2 is connected directly to the paralleled enable inputs of a 74154 1-line-to-16-line decoder/demultiplexer, whose four address inputs are serviced from IORB bits 3 to 6. The 16 outputs are fed to the paralleled G2 enable inputs of each of 16 74LS138 3-line-to-8-line decoders whose address inputs are serviced (via buffers) from bits 0 to 2 of IORB. Each 74LS138 has 8 outputs providing a total of $16 \times 8 = 128$ outputs.

Although the physical configuration of the hardware shows a high degree of symmetry, its mode of *operation* is rather less symmetrical. Whereas each input that is read can be either a '0' or a '1', each output in its normal (inactive) state is always a '1'. Only when an output is selected and enabled (addressed) does it becomes a '0'. And in practice this '0' is short-lived for the output will return to being a '1' a few microseconds later when the computer proceeds to its next operation. This brief negative pulse, however, is more than adequate to satisfy the needs of our application. When an output is to be addressed first its address is set up on IORB bits 0 to 6 and then CB2 is taken low by making bits 7, 6 and 5 of &FE6C respectively a '1', '1' and '0'. CB2 is connected to the paralleled G2 enable inputs of the 74154 which now in turn enables whichever of the 16 74LS138s is addressed by IORB bits 3 to 6. The enabled 74LS138 will now activate one of its outputs as determined by IORB bits 0 to 2. It is essential to ensure that the next operation is to *disable* the 'write' operation by taking CB2 high again, before the address bits are changed. If the address bits are changed while CB2 is still low data will be sent to outputs where it is *not* wanted — with spectacular results!

This reveals another difference between the operation of the two sides of the interface — the 'write' operation is continuous to the currently addressed output as long as CB2 is 'low', while the 'read' operation only takes place at the instant that the contents of &FE60 are accessed and copied into another part of the computer. While in the 'read' mode the address lines can be manipulated *ad lib* without any danger of undesirable effects. For this reason the 'read' mode is the default (normal) mode.

At the expense of the delightful symmetry of our interface it is possible to modify the output side of the device to give 256 outputs. This enables the maximum number of zones to be increased to 256/(controllers + 1). Bit 7 of IORB is used as an eighth address bit when in the 'write' mode; bits 4 to 7 serve a 'master' 74154's address inputs; its 16 outputs in turn enable each of 16 more 74154s whose address inputs are all serviced via buffers from IORB bits 0 to 3. This gives a total of 16 × 16 = 256 outputs. Some considerable modification to the software would be needed since IORB would sometimes be configured as all outputs and sometimes as part input/part output. Also an open-collector device would be needed between IORB bit 7 and the output of the 74150; its output must be held high during 'write' operations to prevent interference with addressing. (Figure 5.2 shows how this could be done.)

Practical considerations

Figure 5.1 may look daunting. It prescribes a 74150 and a 74154, both 24-pin devices, and no fewer than 16 each 74LS151s and 74LS138s. But you only need *all* of these if you want *all* 128 inputs and 128 outputs. You may decide that you don't need every one of those — in which case you may well be able to get away with fewer 74LS151s and 74LS138s. And if you *do* underestimate your requirement you can always add more later (subject to a maximum of 16 each and to there being enough room on the circuit board).

Supposing for instance that your layout has only six zones, five significant turnouts and three controllers. You will need only 6 + 5

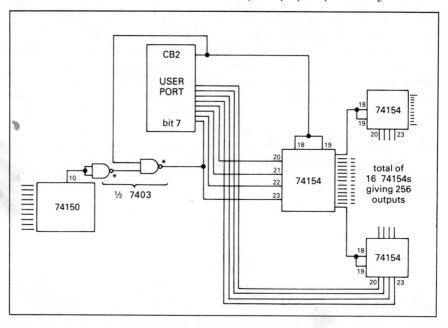

Figure 5.2 *Modification required to part of the circuit in Figure 5.1 to increase the maximum possible number of outputs to 256.*

+ 3 = 14 inputs so just two 74LS151s will suffice (and will allow you two spare inputs for expansion).

You are likely to need more outputs than inputs, even though outputs generally have only one function, *viz*, to service the relays that connect the zones to the controllers. For instance, in the layout considered above, assuming that each of the six zones is to have access to each of the three controllers, you will need 6 × 3 = 18 relays. Since, as we have seen, the outputs from the interface consist of very brief negative-going pulses, the relays must be driven via latching circuits, the simplest of which consist of a pair of NAND gates as shown in Figure 5.3.

An alternative, possibly cheaper since it may be possible to drive the relay direct, is the familiar 555 timer set up as an interval timer having its period as infinity. Offering greater noise immunity, this circuit is shown in Figure 5.4. Each latch has two inputs, the *set* input and the *reset* input. A pulse applied to the *set* input turns the relay on and a pulse applied to the *reset* input turns it off. It may

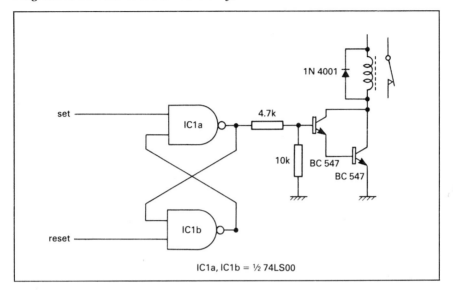

Figure 5.3 *A TTL-based set/reset latch driving a relay for controller switching operations.*

seem therefore that each of the zones on our layout will need to be serviced by *six* outputs, three sets and three resets, making a total of 6 × 6 = 36 outputs. In practice the three resets can be paralleled (Figure 5.5) so that only four outputs per zone are needed. Thus the grand total is 24 outputs which can be provided by three 74LS138s.

The inputs to the interface are standard TTL and can be serviced from any source that is capable of sinking 1mA or more with a voltage drop not exceeding 0.8V. Suitable inputs include the open collectors of npn transistors having emitters grounded to the common return, switch or relay contacts to common return and TTL outputs (open collector or totem-pole). Note that there *must* be a common return to the computer 'ground'. Also, unless the input is serviced from a totem-pole-type TTL output there should be a pull-up resistor from the input to +5V. Its value is not critical but typically is in the region 2K2 to 10K. Omission of the pull-up resistor is unlikely to cause catastrophic results but may lead to a greater susceptibility to interference from electrical equipment such as a nearby model railway!

Outputs from the interface are standard TTL totem-pole type and consist of a very brief negative-going pulse capable of sinking up to

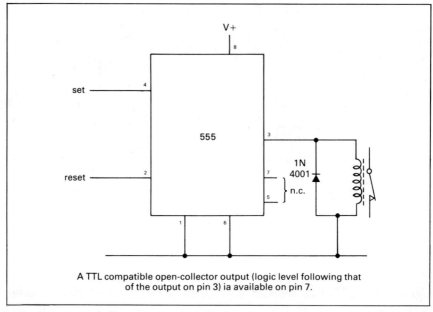

A TTL compatible open-collector output (logic level following that
of the output on pin 3) ia available on pin 7.

Above Figure 5.4 *A preferable set/reset latch — preferable because of its greater noise immunity and the i.c. can drive many relays direct.*

Below Figure 5.5. *Groups of relay drives ganged together sharing a common reset line which the PCC system regards as 'controller 0'.*

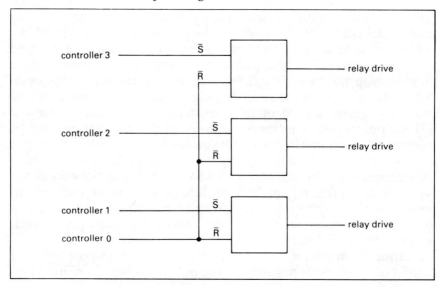

about 8 mA. Because of their nature these outputs are best suited to servicing TTL or similar inputs, as in the set/reset latches shown in Figures 5.3 and 5.4.

The Software

The interface just described is universal, ie, it is the same (subject to the variations mentioned) for any layout. All the 'customizing' for the user's individual layout comes in the software. And even then, the machine-code program that performs the PCC logic is universal — the user variations are in the surrounding BASIC program and in the data which both programs access.

To understand how this PCC system functions imagine yourself as the operator of a traditional cab-controlled layout. You may find yourself thinking, 'The local train is in zone 3 and it's approaching Castle Junction. The turnout is set for the branch so the train will shortly move into zone 12. Since this train is on controller 2 I must now switch zone 12 to controller 2.' The software must enable the computer to do all this thinking for itself.

The first step towards setting up your software sounds a little trite but in practice it's quite an aid to logical thinking. Draw a diagram of your layout clearly showing the relative positions of the control zones and significant turnouts. Next number your control zones, starting with 1. Also indicate on the map by an arrow in each zone the direction in which a train moves when the controller is set for forward movement. Also number the significant turnouts, starting at 1 and, for clarity, prefixing each number with a 'T'.

Figure 5.6 *Plan of the simple hypothetical layout used in our example.*

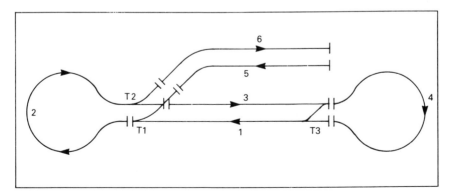

Where a pair of turnouts is ganged for simultaneous operation, eg, at a crossover, one 'T' number will suffice for the pair. The result for a simple layout is shown in Figure 5.6.

The example shows six control zones and three significant turnouts, T3 being a ganged pair. You must also decide at this time how many controllers you intend to use. For this example let's assume two (three would make for overcrowding on a six-zone layout and one would not need PCC). We can now assess our hardware needs: 6 + 3 + 2 = 11 inputs and 6 × 3 = 18 outputs. This means two 74LS151s giving us 16 input addressed lines (numbered 0 to 15) and three 74LS138s giving us 24 output lines (numbered 0 to 23).

Next we must allocate addresses to our inputs and outputs. First the inputs — they're easier. We have the inputs from each zone's track circuit, six in all. For simplicity let's allocate them addresses 1 to 6. Then there are the three turnout direction contacts — let's call them 13, 14 and 15. Lastly there are two controller direction contacts — let's call them 9 and 10.

So we can summarize our input addresses by the following table:

0 not allocated
1 zone 1 occupancy
2 ''   2   ''
3 ''   3   ''
4 ''   4   ''
5 ''   5   ''
6 ''   6   ''
7 not allocated
8 ''   ''
9 controller 1 direction
10   ''   2   ''
11 not allocated
12 ''   ''
13 turnout 1 setting
14   ''   2   ''
15   ''   3   ''

There are 18 outputs since for each of six zones we must send data to (1) connect controller 1, (2) connect controller 2 and (3) connect controller 0. Of course, we don't have a controller 0 — this is just a shorthand way of saying 'activate the common reset line so that neither controller 1 nor controller 2 is connected'. As we have seen there are 24 output lines available. It makes the software rather easier if we organize these so that the three least significant bits of the address code (you'll need to be fully conversant with binary code to understand all that follows) represent the zone number and the next two bits the controller number. So we get:

spare	con.	zone			
0 0 0	0 0	0 0 0 =	0	not allocated	
0 0 0	0 0	0 0 1 =	1	controller 0 to zone 1	
0 0 0	0 0	0 1 0 =	2	'' 0 '' ''	2
0 0 0	0 0	0 1 1 =	3	'' 0 '' ''	3
0 0 0	0 0	1 0 0 =	4	'' 0 '' ''	4
0 0 0	0 0	1 0 1 =	5	'' 0 '' ''	5
0 0 0	0 0	1 1 0 =	6	'' 0 '' ''	6
0 0 0	0 0	1 1 1 =	7	not allocated	
0 0 0	0 1	0 0 0 =	8	'' ''	
0 0 0	0 1	0 0 1 =	9	controller 1 to zone 1	
0 0 0	0 1	0 1 0 =	10	'' 1 '' ''	2
0 0 0	0 1	0 1 1 =	11	'' 1 '' ''	3
0 0 0	0 1	1 0 0 =	12	'' 1 '' ''	4
0 0 0	0 1	1 0 1 =	13	'' 1 '' ''	5
0 0 0	0 1	1 1 0 =	14	'' 1 '' ''	6
0 0 0	0 1	1 1 1 =	15	not allocated	
0 0 0	1 0	0 0 0 =	16	'' ''	
0 0 0	1 0	0 0 1 =	17	controller 2 to zone 1	
0 0 0	1 0	0 1 0 =	18	'' 2 '' ''	2
0 0 0	1 0	0 1 1 =	19	'' 2 '' ''	3
0 0 0	1 0	1 0 0 =	20	'' 2 '' ''	4
0 0 0	1 0	1 0 1 =	21	'' 2 '' ''	5
0 0 0	1 0	1 1 0 =	22	'' 2 '' ''	6
0 0 0	1 0	1 1 1 =	23	not allocated	

Now the fun really begins — and it would be even more fun if the layout were more complex! We have to construct a pair of 'look-up tables'. The first, the 'Turnout Table', will tell us the address of the next turnout that the train will come to (given the current zone number and controller direction). This assumes, as on our simple layout, that there is never more than one significant turnout at the end of each zone. If there is, the Turnout Table will become considerably more complex. The second, the Layout Table, tells us which zone the train will next enter, given the current zone number, controller direction and next turnout setting. The first, for our simple layout, could take the form of a two-dimensional array and the second a three-dimensional array. In practice we are going to poke them straight into a special area of memory, indexing them in much the same way as we arranged the interface's output addresses. This uses rather less memory than do BASIC arrays and is also easier for the machine code to access.

Turnout Table

Zone	Forwards	Reverse
1	1 (13)	3 (15)
2	2 (14)	1 (13)
3	3 (15)	2 (14)
4	3 (15)	3 (15)
5	1 (13)	0 (0)
6	0 (0)	2 (14)

Note the '0's. A '0' in a look-up table in this program generally indicates something that is non-existent (like controller 0) or that is impossible or illegal. In this table it means that there is no such turnout. The numbers in brackets represent the address numbers that must be poked into memory.

We can now proceed to out Layout Table which for our simple layout is as follows. We assume that each turnout's contacts deliver a '1' if set for the main line and a '0' if set for the branch (or crossover at T3).

Layout Table

Present zone	Forwards turnout 1	Forwards turnout 0	Reverse turnout 1	Reverse turnout 0
1	2	0	4	4
2	3	6	1	5
3	4	0	2	0
4	1	0	3	1
5	0	2	0	0
6	0	0	0	2

There are two ways that these tables can be poked into memory. On any BBC Micro you can use indirection indicators. Thus the Turnout Table could be treated as follows:

```
10 DIM turnout 11
20 !turnout=&0F0D0D0E
30 turnout!4=&0E0F0F0F
40 turnout!8=&000D0E00
```

The alternative, which is only available if your BBC Micro has Level-2 BASIC, is to use the EQUate operation within Assembly language. The following shows also how the more complex Layout Table can be entered:

```
100 [OPT pass
110 .turnout EQUD &0F0D0D0E
120 EQUD &0E0F0F0F
130 EQUD &000D0E00
140 .layout EQUD &04040002
150 EQUD &05010603
160 EQUD &00020004
170 EQUD &01030001
180 EQUD &00000200
190 EQUD &02000000
200 ]
```

The Program

The main body of the program is a continuous loop which accesses each of the zones in turn, checks to see what action needs to be taken and takes it. It also checks to see if the operator wishes to feed in any data and it warns him of any hazardous situations.

Central to the program is the *zone status byte* (ZSB), a single byte, one for each zone, which carries all the necessary data about that zone's current status. The zone status byte is made up as shown in Figure 5.7.

The zone management routine begins with the program checking to see if the zone is isolated, ie, if but 7 of the ZSB is set. If it is, the only necessary action is to 'connect controller 0' to that zone whereupon the routine ends.

If the zone is *not* isolated, the program checks the relevant track circuit to see if there is a train present. It then sets bit 6 of the ZSB if there is a train present or resets it if vacant. If vacant it 'connects controller 0', puts 0s into bits 0 to 2 of the ZSB and the routine ends.

If there is a train present it next asks which controller, if any, is connected to it by examining bits 0 to 2 of the ZSB. If these contain the number of a 'legal' controller (ie, one that exists) it sends to the interface to connect that controller. If it returns a 0 (no controller connected) or an illegal number (eg, 7 when there are only two controllers in use) it then asks 'Am I expecting a train in this zone?' by examining bits 3 to 5 of the ZSB. If these contain the number of a valid controller, that number is transferred to bits 0 to 2 and that controller is connected. If bits 3 to 5 contain 0 or an illegal number the program will issue an 'Unauthorized train in Zone X' error and the routine will end. The operator can use the keyboard to enter the requested controller number into bits 3 to 5.

If the routine has resulted in a controller being connected (or reconnected) the program will now determine which zone the train will enter next. This is where our look-up tables come in. First it checks which controller is connected (ZSB bits 0 to 2) and then it looks up the address of the controller's direction contacts (by adding 8 to the controller number in our program — though this could vary); from this it goes to the Turnout Table to get the address of the contacts of the next turnout. Then by quadrupling the current zone number, adding double the direction and adding the turnout setting it gets the next zone number from the Layout Table. If the train is approaching a terminus, there will be no next zone so the Layout Table will return a 0. The program will then issue a 'Caution in Zone X' error and the routine exits. Like a signal showing a caution aspect, this is a warning to the operator to be ready to stop his train.

If the table returns a valid zone number the program looks at that zone's ZSB. First it checks if the zone is isolated by looking at bit 7. If the zone is isolated the program issues a 'Caution in Zone X: Zone Y not available' error. If the zone is not isolated, the program now checks to see if the zone is occupied by looking at bit 6. If it is not occupied, our current train's controller number is written into bits 3 to 5 of the new zone's ZSB to tell it that a train is expecting to enter. If it is occupied, the number of the controller currently connected to that zone is checked (bits 0 to 2). If this is different from the number of the controller connected to the zone under consideration, a 'Caution in Zone X: Zone Y not available' error is generated. If the controller numbers are the same, however, no error is generated and the program continues — this caters for the finite time in which a train occupies two zones when passing from one to the other.

Since these operations all involve manipulations on single bytes of memory and since both speed and memory economy (you may wish to combine this with a MODE2 mimic diagram) are essential, the zone management routine is a machine code program, whose Assembler is listed as PROCassemble in Listing 5.1.

The control loop

The progressive cab control system is itself controlled by the BASIC in lines 100 to 380. The main loop is the REPEAT...UNTIL loop in lines 160 to 290; nested within this is the FOR...TO...NEXT loop in lines 170 to 270. On each pass of the main loop the resident integer variable X% passes through all values from 1 to the number of zones and for each value the machine code routine is called. It was most thoughtful of the designers of BBC BASIC to arrange that when a machine code routine is called from BASIC the microprocessor's X register is automatically set to the least significant byte of X% (and the Y register to Y% and the A register to A%). This provides a very simple method of passing parameters from BASIC to machine code.

A tabular display devotes a line to each zone in order to indicate its current status. The left-hand column (headed 'I') contains an 'I' if that zone is isolated (all zones are isolated when the program is started). The next column headed 'O' contains an 'O' if that zone is occupied. The next column headed 'C' contains the number of the controller currently connected to the zone or '0' if no controller is connected. The next column headed 'D' contains the direction setting ('F' or 'R') of the controller ('F' if no controller is connected). The last column headed 'N' contains the number of the next zone to be entered by the train in that zone or '0' if there is no such train (or zone). The remainder of each line is reserved for error messages, eg, 'Caution! Next zone not available'.

In the form given here two parameters can be controlled from the keyboard. Zones can be isolated or restored and controllers can be assigned to zones. Pressing 'I' will cause the program to ask 'Isolate which zone?'. Pressing 'R' will prompt the question, 'Restore which zone?'. In either event the next number entered will be assumed to be the zone number; the zone status byte will be modified as required. Similarly pressing 'C' will prompt the question 'Which controller?'. Entering a number will prompt the further question 'To which zone?'. Note that in its present form the inputs cater only for single-digit numbers, but the routine could easily be adapted for multi-digit numbers — or you could give your zones letters.

It is important that this kind of program should never be stopped. The machine-code routine must continue to monitor each zone in turn even while the operator is inputting data. You will notice that the input routines do not employ the INPUT or GET statements which would inevitably force the computer to wait — instead the keyboard is checked for keystrokes at the start of the main loop by the INKEY function in line 160. When a keystroke is detected the main loop is temporarily suspended at line 290 and the significance of the keystroke analysed.

The program is very open indeed to extension and modification. It could be combined with the layout mimic diagram (Chapter 4) or turnout control (Chapter 9). It is even possible to modify the program so that it will run happily without the model railway at all as a 'model of a model'!

Listing for progressive cab control

```
  10 REM PROGRESSIVE CAB CONTROL
  20 REM ROGER AMOS 23 OCT 1985
  30 MODE7
  40 REM N%=number of zones
  50 N%=6
  60 REM &70 contains number of controllers + 1
  70 ?&70=3
  80 REM Configure IORB for input on bit 7, output on bits 0
to 6
  90 ?&FE62=127
 100 port=&FE60:pcr=&FE6C:utflag=&71:cautflag=&72:ocflag=&73
:temp=&8F :!&71=0
 110 DIMzone N%, pcc 400:FORX%=1TON%:zone?X%=0:NEXT
 120 PROCassemble
 130 MODE7:VDU23;8202;0;0;0;:FORX%=1TON%:PRINTTAB(0,X%);"Zon
e ";X%;:VDU131,73,129,32,130,48,132,32,133,32,134:NEXT
 140 PRINTTAB(7,0);"I O C D N Messages"
 150 PROCclear
 160 REPEAT:A$=INKEY$(0)
 170 P%=POS:V%=VPOS:FORX%=1TON%
 180 CALL pcc
 190 PRINTTAB(11,X%);zone?X% AND7
 200 VDU31,9,X%:IFzone?X% AND64 PRINT"O";ELSEVDU32
 210 IF?utflag PRINTTAB(17,X%);"Unauthorised train"
 220 IF?cautflag PRINTTAB(17,X%);"Caution!"
 230 IF?ocflag PRINTTAB(26,X%);"Next zone n/a"
```

```
   240 PRINTTAB( 15,X% );?&74 :?&74=0
   250 IF!&71=0PRINTTAB( 17,X% );SPC( 23 )
   260 VDU31 ,13,X% :IF?&75 PRINT"R" :ELSEPRINT"F"
   270 NEXTX%
   280 VDU31 ,P% ,V%
   290 UNTILA$<>""
   300 IFA$="I"ORA$="i"PRINTTAB( 0,10 );"Isolate which zone? ";:
 I%=TRUE :GOTO160
   310 IFI%PRINTA$:z%=VAL( A$ ):IFz%>N%GOTO150 :ELSEIFI%zone?z%=z
 one?z%OR128 :PRINTTAB( 7,z% );"I" :GOTO150
   320 IFA$="R"ORA$="r"PRINTTAB( 0,10 );"Restore which zone? ";:
 R%=TRUE :GOTO160
   330 IFR%PRINTA$:z%=VAL( A$ ):IFz%>N%GOTO150 :ELSEIFR%zone?z%=z
 one?z%AND127 :PRINTTAB( 7,z% );" " :GOTO150
   340 IFA$="C"ORA$="c"PRINTTAB( 0,10 );"Which controller? ";:C%
 =TRUE :GOTO160
   350 IFT%PRINTA$:z%=VAL( A$ ):IFz%>N%GOTO150 :ELSEIFT%zone?z%=z
 one?z%AND199 :zone?z%=zone?z%OR( 8*c% ):GOTO150
   360 IFC%PRINTA$:;c%=VAL( A$ ):IFc%>?&70GOTO150 :ELSEIFC%PRINT"
  To which zone? ";:T%=TRUE :GOTO160
   370 GOTO150
   380 DEFPROCclear :PRINTTAB( 0,10 );SPC( 40 ):I%=0 :R%=0 :E%=0 :O%=0
 :C%=0 :T%=0 :D%=0 :ENDPROC
   390 DEFPROCassemble
   400 FORpass=0TO3STEP3 :P%=pcc
   410 [OPTpass
   420 LDAzone,X :PHA \get ZSB and save it
   430 AND#128 :BEQocc \check if zone isolated
   440 PLA :JMPdisconnect \if isolated restore ZSB
   450 .occ STXport :LDAport :AND#128 :BEQtis \read zone's track
 circuit
   460 PLA :AND#56 \if empty reset bits 0-3/6/7
   470 .disconnect STXport :JSRsend :JMPexit \send 'connect cont
 roller 0'
   480 .tis PLA :ORA#64 :PHA \set bit 6 and save
   490 AND#7 :BEQtraindue :CMP&70 :BCStraindue \see if ZSB contai
 ns legal controller
   500 PLA :JMP connect \if legal restore
   510 .traindue PLA :PHA :LSRA :LSRA :LSRA :AND#7 :BEQunauth :CMP&70
 :BCSunauth \see if bits 3-5 point to legal controller
   520 TAY :PLA :TYA :ORA#64 :JMPconnect \kill old ZSB and set up
 new one
   530 .unauth STXutflag :PLA \generate 'unauthorised train' er
 ror
   540 .exit STAzone,X :RTS
   550 .connect STXtemp \put zone number in an accessible loca
 tion
   560 PHA :ASLA :ASLA :ASLA \shunt controller number into bits 3
 -5
   570 AND#63 :CLC :ADCtemp :STAport :JSRsend \add zone number and
```

```
    send data
    580 PLA:PHA:AND#7:CLC:ADC#8:STAport \get controller directi
on address and ...
    590 LDY#0:LDAport:AND#128:BEQdone:LDY#1 \Y now contains dir
ection
    600 .done STYtemp:STY&75:TXA:ASLA:CLC:ADCtemp:LDYtemp \Y no
w contains direction + 2*zone number
    610 LDAturnout,Y \accumulator contains address of next tur
nout
    620 STAport:LDY#0:ASLtemp:LDAport:AND#128:BEQnil:LDY#1 \Y c
ontains turnout setting, temp contains 2*direction
    630 .nil TXA:ASLA:ASLA:CLC:ADCtemp:STYtemp:CLC:ADCtemp:TAY
\Y contains offset for layout table
    640 LDA layout,Y:BNEnotzero \is next zone number valid?
    650 STXcautflag:PLA:JMPexit \if zero generate "caution" err
or
    660 .notzero TAY:LDAzone,Y:STY&74 \load next zone's ZSB
    670 AND#128:BEQnotisol \is next zone isolated?
    680 .generr STXcautflag:STYocflag:PLA:JMPexit \generate "ca
ution - next zone not available" error
    690 .notisol LDAzone,Y:AND#64:BEQnotocc \is next zone occup
ied?
    700 LDAzone,Y:AND#7:STAtemp:LDAzone,X:AND#7:CMPtemp:BEQnoto
cc \if occupied, see if same controller number
    710 JMPgenerr \if different generate error
    720 .notocc LDAzone,Y:AND#199:STAzone,Y \kill bits 3-5 of n
ext ZSB
    730 LDAzone,X:AND#7:ASLA:ASLA:ASLA:ORAzone,Y:STAzone,Y \wri
te current controller in bits 3-5 of next ZSB
    740 PLA:JMPexit \restore ZSB, end
    750 .send PHA:LDApcr:AND#223:STApcr:ORA#32:STApcr:PLA:RTS \
activate output addressed by IORB bits 0-6
    760 .turnout EQUD&0F0D0D0E
    770 EQUD&0E0F0F0F
    780 EQUD&000D0E00
    790 EQUD&000D0E00
    800 .layout EQUD&04040002
    810 EQUD&05010603
    820 EQUD&00020004
    830 EQUD&01030001
    840 EQUD&00000200
    850 EQUD&02000000
    860 ]
    870 NEXTpass
    880 ENDPROC
```

Chapter 6

Track-to-computer interface

So far the communications between layout and computer considered in this book have all been *digital*, that is they have used combinations of binary digits each of which is either 'on' (high) or 'off' (low). It is in such (essentially simple!) 'bits' of data that computers work.

The BBC Micro, however, is fitted with a set of analogue-to-digital converters (ADCs) which take an input having a voltage which may vary over a range of values and produce a proportional digital output. Such interfaces are widely available for the Spectrum as add-ons since they are an essential prerequisite of the 'joysticks' that are used with certain computer games. For our purposes, however, the value of ADCs is that they allow us to take an analogue voltage, such as the voltage delivered by a pure dc controller, and feed that to the computer so that it can provide speed-proportional effects. This chapter describes a steam sound ('chuffer') related to train speed — or at least to controller voltage.

The first stage is to translate the track voltage (normally $+/- 12v$) to a level and polarity acceptable to the BBC's analogue port, ie, in the range 0 to 1.8v. Any inputs exceeding this may cause internal damage to the computer. An input of 1.8v will give a digital value of 65520.

The simple circuit to achieve this is shown in Figure 6.1. This consists of a diode bridge (D1-4), to rectify the track voltage, the output being rectified by C1. If you use a pure dc controller C1 is not required. If, however, you use a PWM or unsmoothed dc controller C1 should be included. A suitable value is 10µF with a voltage rating of 63v.

The smoothed signal is next fed to a differential amplifier, IC1. A differential amplifier amplifies (or in this case attenuates) the difference in voltage between two points and gives an output rela-

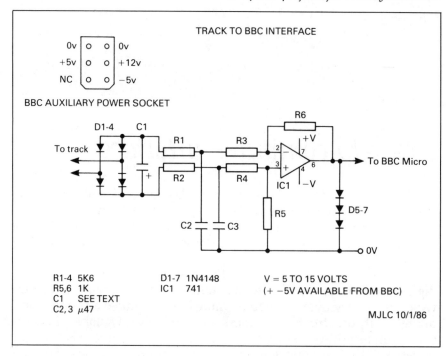

Figure 6.1 *A track-to-BBC analogue-to-digital interface used in this project as a speed-proportional 'chuffer'.*

tive to ground. In this application it usefully eliminates the need to connect the computer's 0v line to the layout earth.

The gain of a differential amplifier is given by:

$$G = R_{feedback}/R_{input}$$

In this case $R_{feedback}$ is R6, and R_{input} is R1+R3, giving a gain of 0.09. So an input of 12v will give an output of 1.08v. Any input voltage up to 20v is permissible since this is the input needed to give the maximum output of 1.8v. The input resistors R1/R3 and R2/R4 are split and combined with C2 and C3 to form input filters to remove any nasty spikes from the layout. The amplifier output is clamped to a maximum of 2.1v by diode chain D5-7, to prevent excessive voltages entering the BBC Micro.

Inputs to the analogue port are made via a 15-way D-socket. A matching plug should be purchased and the input connection made to pin 15. This is the leftmost pin on the bottom row when looking from the wiring side (it may even be numbered on the plug).

As the maximum output of the circuit is only 1.8v, it may be run off the BBC's internal +/– 5v supply. This is available on the auxiliary power connector on the underside of the machine. The pinout is illustrated on the circuit diagram.

A simple program to produce a 'chuff' effect is given below.

```
 10 CLS
 20 MULT=1.75
 30 *FX16,1
 40 ENVELOPE1,1,0,0,0,75,75,75,100,-5,-50,-1,126,50
 50 SOUND&0010,1,5,3
 60 A%=65000-ADVAL(1)*MULT
 70 IF A%>57000 THEN SOUND0,-2,4,10: GOTO60
 80 FORI=1TOA%/35
 90   NEXT
100 GOTO 50
```

Line 20 sets a multiplier variable to determine the ratio between train speed and chuff rate. The value given was found to be fine for many model locos but may need some adjustment depending on the locos in use — alter this to taste.

Line 30 sets the ADC system to use only channel 1 (there are four channels) to increase speed. Line 40 sets the chuff envelope. Line 50 generates a chuff. Line 60 calculates a variable proportional to train speed. Line 70 works out if the train is stationary and, if so, generates a hiss, bypassing the chuff generator. The value 57000 may need adjusting to suit your individual locos. Line 80 generates a delay that decreases with train speed. Line 100 repeats the loop.

Chapter 7

A user port for the Spectrum

As we have seen, the BBC Micro (Model B) contains a built-in 8-bit
user port which allows it to be connected directly to other digital
equipment — in our case, on our layouts. The Spectrum contains
no such interface but does have a bus output to which a separate
user-port interface can be connected. The authors gratefully
acknowledge their indebtedness to Dr John Down whose work,
described in a talk to the Model Electronic Railway Group in
November 1985, is the basis of this and the next chapters.

A circuit diagram of the interface is given in Figure 7.1. The interface works as follows. In the Spectrum memory map (Figure 7.2)
the lowest 16k is occupied by ROM (read-only memory) with the
next 16k (up to 32k total) or 48k (up to 64k total) occupied by RAM
(random-access memory). Whether 16k or 48k of RAM is present
depends on the version of the Spectrum — for our purposes the
difference is immaterial.

Further examination of the ROM will show that it is full of the
firmware that supports the overall operating system, including the
BASIC interpreter and its routines. The top of ROM contains a
representation of the entire character set. Sandwiched between the
bottom of this and the top of the BASIC handler lie several hundred
bytes of unused ROM — these contain, effectively the value 255
(&FF). The interface is 'mapped' into this area. That is to say, the
address bus, when addressing memory, is also connected to the
interface in such a fashion that the interface input or output byte is
also addressed. The interface, when addressed, responds by
returning a signal to the computer which disables the ROM.

In this way the computer is 'fooled' into thinking that the interface is an area of memory into which data can be written and from
which data can be read in the normal manner. Our interface uses
the memory location 15608 (&3CF8) as the address of its output
byte.

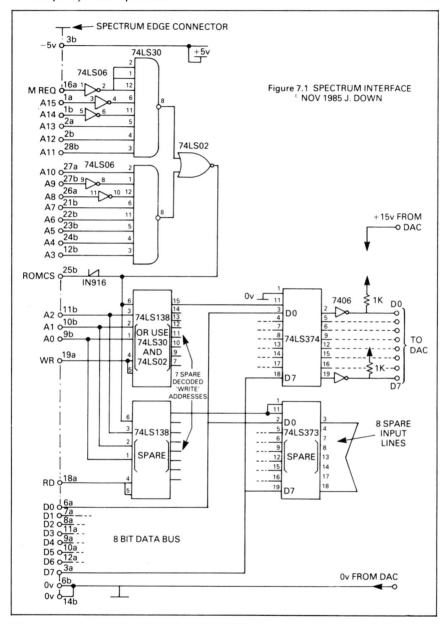

Figure 7.1 An interface that gives the ZX Spectrum a very versatile user port.

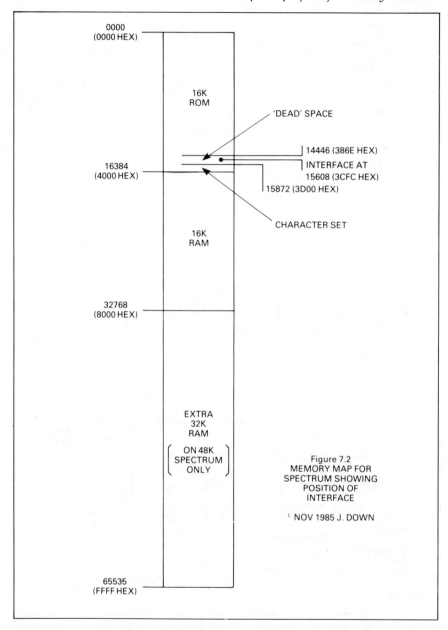

0000
(0000 HEX)

16K
ROM

'DEAD' SPACE

14446 (386E HEX)

16384
(4000 HEX)

INTERFACE AT
15608 (3CFC HEX)

15872 (3D00 HEX)

CHARACTER SET

16K
RAM

32768
(8000 HEX)

EXTRA
32K
RAM

ON 48K
SPECTRUM
ONLY

Figure 7.2
MEMORY MAP FOR
SPECTRUM SHOWING
POSITION OF
INTERFACE

NOV 1985 J. DOWN

65535
(FFFF HEX)

Figure 7.2 ZX Spectrum memory map showing the position at which the user port interface is 'mapped in'.

The gates in the interface establish when the signal lines MREQ' and WR' are simultaneously low and that the 16 address lines A0 to A15 signal the address &3CF8, ie, that the computer wants to write data into location &3CF8. They do this by inverting those address bits where a '0' is needed so that the address is defined uniquely by 16 '1's. In fact the bottom three bits are decoded into eight addresses starting from &3CF8 using the 74LS138 so that only A8, A9, A14 and A15 specifically need inverting. The control signals MREQ' and WR' also need inversion. Note the signal line ROMCS' (ie, not-ROM-chip-select) which returns to the computer to disable the ROM.

Once the control signals and address are decoded, they are fed to the octal latch (74LS374) to 'capture' the data present on the data bus (D0 to D7). These data form the output from the user port. The process of reading data from the interface input into the computer is essentially the reverse of the same process, except that the RD' and MREQ' control signals must be taken low.

Chapter 8

Digital-to-analogue controller

There are essentially two techniques available in the design of electronic controllers (throttles) for model railways: *closed-loop control* where a typically steady dc output is compared with an analogue input and *pulse-width modulation* where the output consists of pulses of full power whose duration is varied to control train speed. These two techniques represent the analogue and the digital approach respectively.

Oddly enough it is the analogue (closed-loop) technique that offers the most scope for the (digital) computer user. While it is theoretically possible to use a computer as a pulse-width-modulator in practice the application is so fraught with difficulties as to be — to all intents and purposes — impossible.*

Digital-to-analogue interfaces, in contrast, can be constructed fairly simply and can be used as the basis of a closed-loop-type controller driven from the output of an 8-bit user port. The circuit described in this chapter was developed by Dr John Down for use with his Spectrum user port described in the last chapter, but could easily be adapted for use with any computer.

The hardware
The circuit diagram of the controller is given in Figure 8.1. The lowest seven bits of its input byte are connected to a weighted set of resistors with values of 64k, 32k, 16k, 8k, 4k, 2k, and 1k.

---

*The trouble is that BASIC is too slow, even on the BBC, to provide PWM control at the 100 Hz or so that is needed for smooth control of model trains. Machine code has more than adequate speed, but is difficult to control since the microprocessor is perpetually being 'interrupted' to perform other tasks, eg, updating the on-board clocks. The BBC does contain a timer that is incremented at 1 MHz, but repeated attempts by the authors to develop routines that made use of this only ever led to the computer 'locking up'. Perhaps it is not insignificant that *The Advanced User Guide for the BBC Micro*, while devoting five pages to the 1 MHz timer (pp 404-408), does not actually give an application program.

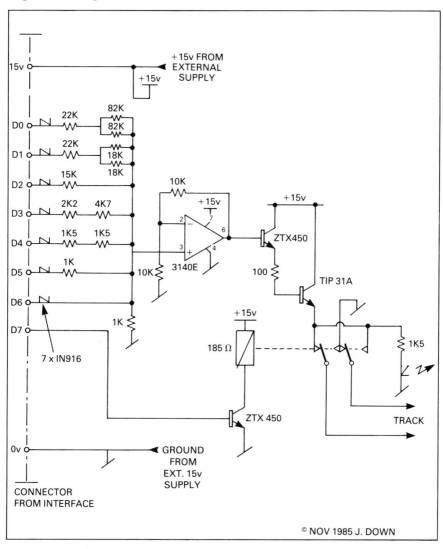

Figure 8.1 *Digital-to-analogue loco controller: designed for the Spectrum but equally applicable to the BBC or any machine having an 8-bit user port.*

These values are actually reduced by 1k each to allow for the 1k pull-up resistor in the latch buffer. Each resistor limb has a diode to prevent mutual interference and the summing point feeds a CA3140E operational amplifier fitted with a 10k feedback resistor.

Traditionalists may prefer to use the 741 and its variants if they so wish. The output voltage from the op amp is Vcc.1k/R where R is the effective load resistance switched in. The output can thus be controlled in $2^7 = 127$ voltage steps, which compares favourably with the 15 steps provided by Hornby's Zero-1.

The output of the op amp drives a traditional Darlington pair, the choice of devices being uncritical. The eighth bit, D7, drives a two-pole changeover relay via a single transistor to provide a reversing facility.

It has been pointed out that the output of the resistor network is in fact not perfectly linear, but the Darlington also introduces non-linearities through its introduction of a 1.4V drop. Nevertheless the system provides a fine control of train speed.

The software

Originally the system was developed using the Spectrum as a feasibility study only. Consequently the software was devised as a series of informal fragments which can be mixed and modified according to the user's requirements. However, the following precautions are advised:

1. The interface latch is regularly updated, even if the data are unchanged. This is to reduce the possibility of corruption caused for example by electrical interference.

2. The keyboard is regularly scanned 'on the fly' for keystrokes.

Note that speed is set in the range 0 to 127 and that direction is set by adding or subtracting 128. Note also that in the Spectrum interface described in the previous chapter the output is inverted by the 7406 buffer so that, in the Spectrum program that follows the control voltage V is always inverted (255-V) before being poked into the interface. In this program press '1' to brake, '0' to accelerate, 'Q' to emergency stop and 'Q' or 'P' to change direction.

Table 8.1: Controller program (Spectrum)

```
10 LET A=0
20 LET V=0
30 POKE 15608,255-V
50 IF INKEY$="1" THEN LET V=V+1
60 IF INKEY$="0" THEN LET V=V-1
70 IF INKEY$="P" THEN LET V=V-128 : IF V<0 THEN LET V=V+128
80 IF INKEY$="0" THEN LET V=V+128 : IF V>255 THEN LET V=V-12
8
```

```
 90 IF INKEY$="Q" THEN LET V=0
100 IF V<0 THEN LET V=0
110 IF V=126 THEN LET V=125
120 IF V=-127 THEN LET V=128
130 IF V>253 THEN LET V=253
200 PAUSE A
300 GO TO 30
```

BBC users ought to be able to deduce an equivalent program for their machines. It is of course easy to print either alphanumerically or graphically details regarding speed and direction on a VDU screen. With only marginally more complication an input port could read track circuit output and provide various forms of automatic operation.

Chapter 9

Turnout (point) control interface

This simple project provides computer control of up to eight turnouts. It could also be used to operate other mechanical accessories (such as semaphore signals) driven by point motors (switch machines) or similar solenoids. The project could also be extended to operate more than eight turnouts if required.

A useful feature is that the computer interface components may be added to an existing conventional point control system (electric pencil or passing contact switches) without affecting its operation. So computer control can be used when convenient but the layout can be operated conventionally without the computer if desired. This is achieved by placing a computer-controlled electronic switch in parallel with the existing switch or stud.

The interface makes use of the BBC Micro's user port, as does the mimic diagram project in Chapter 4. Whereas the mimic diagram used the port for inputs, this project uses it to output information, ie, data on which point to change and in which direction.

As well as the port data lines, one of the control lines, CB2, is used. This can be programmed to give a pulse whenever data is written to the port lines. Since this pulse lasts only 1 microsecond, not long enough to change a turnout, hardware is needed to extend it to a more useful length.

Only four of the user port data lines are used. These are designated to the following functions:

PB0 Specifies way point is to be set

PB1 ⎫

PB2 ⎬ Specify which point to change

PB3 ⎭

Circuit description

The circuit diagram of the interface is given in Figure 9.1. IC1 is a dual monostable multivibrator, only half of which is used in this application. This stretches the pulse from CB2 to approximately 1 millisecond. The extended pulse enables decoders IC2 and IC3.

IC2 and IC3 are 3-to-8 line decoders, which give a high output on 1 of 8 output lines corresponding to the binary number present on the three input lines. The outputs are only activated when the 3 enable inputs are correct. PB0 provides one of these inputs, selecting one of the decoders depending on the required point direction. The other enable input is provided by the extended CB2 signal. This produces outputs long enough for the point to change. Outputs are provided for eight points, IC2 catering for outputs in one

Figure 9.1 *Turnout control interface.*

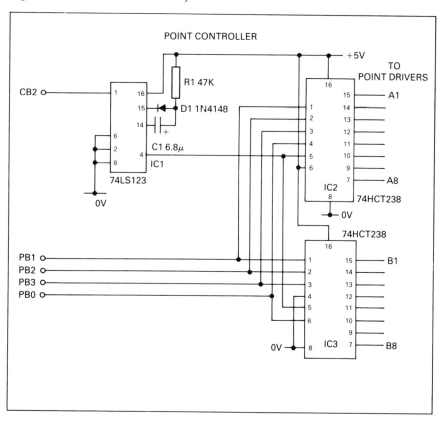

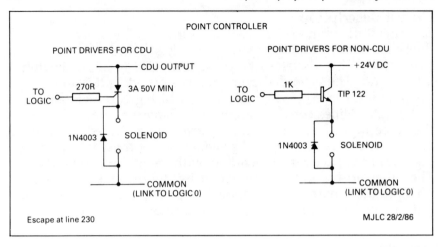

Figure 9.2 *Two ways in which the output of the turnout control interface can be applied to turnout motor solenoids: (left) where a capacitor-discharge unit is used and (right) using a conventional dc supply.*

direction and IC3 outputs in the other direction.

Two alternative methods of driving the point motor solenoids are illustrated in Figure 9.2. If a capacitor-discharge unit (CDU) is being used, a *thyristor* can be used to switch the turnouts. This is a semi-conductor device which, when 'fired', ie, activated by a control pulse, becomes conductive and remains conductive until the supply voltage (in our application the capacitor voltage) falls to a certain low value, whereupon it will switch itself off. Any old thyristor will do provided it is rated at at least 3 amps, 50 volts. Packs of unmarked thyristors can be obtained cheaply from several suppliers, eg, BIPAK, and are a very economical way of obtaining the 16 power devices needed to control eight points.

For a non-CDU system, it is necessary to use a power Darlington as a driver. It may be necessary to increase the output pulse duration by raising the value of R1 to achieve satisfactory switching. 250k should be sufficient, but if not, C1 should be increased to 22μF as well.

In both versions it is necessary to put a 1N4003 diode in parallel with the point motor to protect the driver devices from high voltage spikes when current to the solenoid is cut. As previously mentioned, the driving device can by wired in parallel with any existing switches or studs.

Table 9.1: Example program

```
10 REM SIMPLE POINT CONTROL
20 REM INITIALISE USER PORT
30 REM DDR = ALL OUTPUTS
40 ?&FE62=255
50 REM PCR = CB2 PULSE CONTROL
60 ?&FE6C=&A0
70 REM MAIN LOOP
80 REPEAT
90   CLS
100  INPUT"Point No. (1-8)";point%
110  INPUT"Direction (1,0)";dir%
120  out% = (point%-1)*2 + dir%
130  REM OUTPUT TO USER PORT
140  ?&FE60 = out%
150  UNTIL FALSE
```

This simple program illustrates how to set up the user port for the interface — lines 40 and 60, and how to output the relevant data. This involves calculating a binary number corresponding to the pattern required by the user port. As lines PB1-3 correspond to the point number, this number must be multiplied by 2, and added to either 1 or 0 depending on the setting required. This is done in line 120. Line 140 sends the data to the user port.

The interface could be simply extended by the use of extra decoders and additional lines from the user port to cope with larger numbers (up to 128) of turnouts.

Appendix 1

Useful electronic circuitry

Many of the projects in this book depend upon the presence on the model railway of electronic circuitry to which the computer can be interfaced. This appendix presents a selection of suitable circuitry. Further information may be found in *Practical Electronics for Railway Modellers* and *Practical Electronics for Railway Modellers 2* by Roger Amos (Patrick Stephens Ltd).

Controller
The simple and robust circuit shown in Figure A1.1 is ideally suited for interface work since it presents a high input impedance and can be modified in an infinite number of ways to meet different requirements. Don't worry if you can't obtain a 2N6650 as the output device. Any PNP power Darlington will do or alternatively you can make up your own Darlington using discrete devices. Any PNP power transistor (eg, MJE2955 or PNP3055) may be used for the output transistor — connect a 100R resistor between its base and emitter. For the driver transistor (ie, pre-output stage) any general-purpose PNP transistor will do — suitable types include the BC177, BC212 and BC557. Connect a 1K resistor between its base and emitter. Do not omit the resistors — without them the Darlington will faithfully amplify every picoamp of leakage current from T1 and you will be unable to turn the controller all the way off. The reverse-biased diode shown inside the Darlington ic in the diagram is not essential and may be omitted.

For use from an analogue input simply remove VR1 and use the open end of R1 as an input. Input voltages between 0 and about 18V will give the full control range. If you wish to use a lower range of control voltages — say 0 to 5V — adopt the following modification. In parallel with diode D1 connect a pair of resistors in series. The upper one we shall call Rx and the lower one Ry. Now return

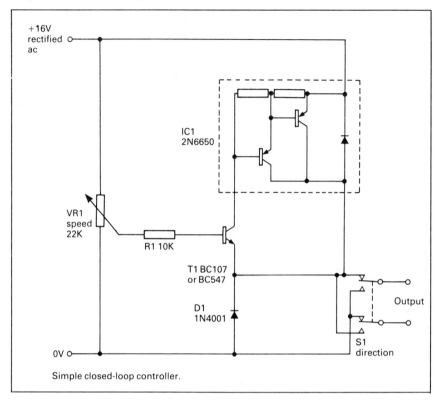

Figure A1.1 *Simple closed-loop controller ideally suited for adaptation for computer projects.*

the emitter of T1 to the junction of these two resistors (Figure A1.2). This ensures that only Ry/(Rx + Ry) of the output voltage is fed back to the comparator (T1). So, if the maximum output voltage is 18V but the maximum input voltage is 5V the ratio of Ry to Rx is easily set; choose values to give a total resistance in the range 5K to 20K. A suitable combination would be 2.7K for Ry and 6.8K for Rx.

If automatic reversing facilities are required all that is needed is to replace S1 in Figure A1.1 by a relay having a minimum of double-pole double-throw (DPDT) contacts. If a modern high-efficiency miniature type is used almost certainly it could be driven by the arrangement shown in Figure A1.3. T1 may be almost any type of general-purpose NPN transistor but for some applications may need to be a Darlington. Any value of power supply may be used to

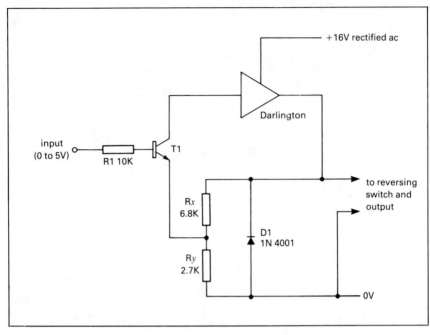

Above Figure A1.2 *Modification of the circuit in Figure A1.1 to give voltage gain; this is determined by the Ratio of Ry to (Rx + Ry).*

Below Figure A1.3 *Relay drive circuitry for reversing: a continuous logical '1' will be needed on the input to hold the relay energized.*

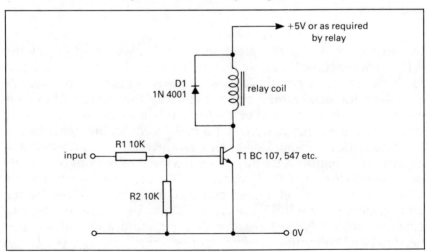

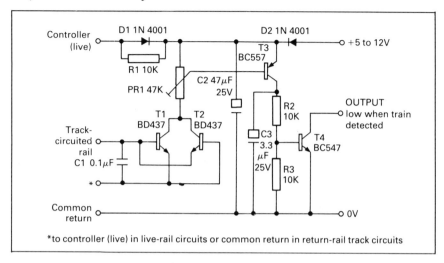

Figure A1.4 *A bidirectional track circuit until for live rail or return rail applications: it delivers a TTL-compatible logical '0' when a train is detected.*

suit the relay's requirements but do not use a higher value than the transistor's rating (most general-purpose types are rated for about 45V).

Train detectors

Two methods of train detection are in common use with a variety of more exotic methods in less common use. *Track circuiting* as on prototype railways detects the presence of a train in a section of line by monitoring the section's electrical conductivity. On model railways of course only locomotives or vehicles fitted with lighting or vehicles specially 'conductivized' are detected, but this is quite adequate for most requirements.

Figure A1.4 shows a general-purpose track-circuit unit which gives a TTL-compatible logical '0' when a train is detected. To use this unit first identify the section to be monitored and then decide whether you wish to monitor the supply to the live rail or the return rail — the unit can be used in either mode. In many existing layouts it is easiest to make track circuiting sections correspond with cab control zones in which traditionally the live rail is switched. It is then usually fairly straightforward to insert the unit into the live rail supply. For a detailed explanation of this unit's operation see Chapter 11 of *Practical Electronics for Railway Modellers 2.*

The alternative method of train detection is to employ track-mounted reed switches operated by magnets attached beneath the trains. The reed switches may be mounted longitudinally, mid-way between the rails, or transversely. The magnets must obviously have similar orientation. The contacts in the reed switch are normally open but close when the switch comes under the influence of a suitable magnet.

A reed switch gives a pulse of output when a train is directly over it. It therefore may be used whenever it is necessary to know if a train is at a certain point. Track circuiting may be emulated, however, by using two reed switches and a set/reset latch. Connect a reed switch at the beginning of the section to the 'set' input of the latch and another at the end of the section (which may also serve as the switch at the start of the next section) to the reset input of the same latch. For bidirectional working it is necessary to have two reed switches at the start and end of each section (see Project 15 of *Practical Electronics for Railway Modellers*.)

A practical difficulty is that reed switches at the ends of long leads that follow a layout's busy trunk routes easily pick up electrical interference so that the bistables, especially if constructed using

Figure A1.5 A reed switch/bistable system that emulates track circuiting: the number of reed switches is doubled if bidirectional running is to be supported.

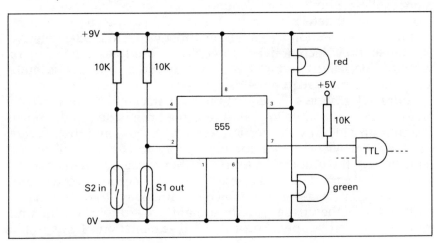

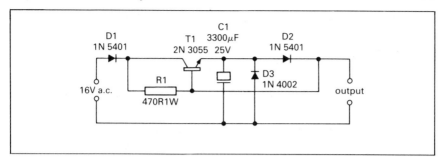

Figure A1.6 *A capacitor discharge unit for turnout control applications: this unit incorporates short-circuit protection.*

TTL gates, are prone to spurious latchings and unlatchings. This can be overcome by the use of the circuit shown in Figure A1.5 where a 555 timer ic using a high (ie higher than 5V) supply voltage. While the 555's regular output (pin 3) is ideal for driving 'grain-of-wheat' bulbs used as signal aspects, pin 7 can be used as an independent TTL-compatible output irrespective of the 555's supply voltage.

Turnout control
Figure A1.6 shows a practical capacitor discharge unit which combines the advantages of rapid capacitor recharge with short-circuit protection. It is ideally suited for use with the turnout control system described in Chapter 9 of this book.

Electrical indication of turnout setting
Some projects, such as progressive cab control (Chapter 5), depend upon the availability of an electrical indication of the way turnouts are set. There are several ways in which such an indication may be obtained:

1. Some turnouts, such as the long obsolete (but still obtainable) Hornby-Dublo live-frog 00/HO types, incorporate a built-in SPDT switch linked mechanically to the turnout tiebar.

2. Peco manufactures a SPDT switch designed to be fitted to the Peco turnout motor.

3. It is quite easy to arrange for a microswitch to be linked to the turnout tiebar.

4. If the turnout is electrically operated, a suitable signal *may* be

available from the driver circuit. If it is computer driven, the existing software may store the turnout setting, otherwise it could doubtless be modified to do so. But these methods, in contrast with (1-3) above, only indicate the *last* automatic setting of the turnout. If the turnout were subsequently manually reset an error would occur. Methods (1-3) monitor the current mechanical status of the turnout.

5. Some passing-contact switches intended for the electric operation of turnout motors incorporate SPDT contacts. The same limitation applies as to (4) above.

6. Turnouts can be operated perfectly satisfactorily by mechanical operation from ex-Post Office drawstop switches which have DPDT contacts.

Appendix 2

Internal workings of microcomputers

A kind of mystique hangs over the whole subject of microcomputers — and indeed of computers in general — as though they represent some totally unique technology. In fact they do not. Microcomputers are simply the natural extension of logic circuitry such as the 74 and 74LS transistor/transistor logic (TTL) that have been at the disposal of electronics hobbyists for nearly twenty years. Readers who are not familiar with this technology are advised to read Appendix 4 in *Practical Electronics for Railway Modellers 2* by Roger Amos.

TTL makes it feasible to build up *dedicated* circuitry for performing simple logical and arithmetical processes. *Dedicated* means 'set apart for one purpose only'. Thus the circuitry that you build to drive a four-aspect signal at a complex junction may do its job admirably, but it would be of little use if you wanted it to add two numbers together.

With a little ingenuity, however, it is possible to design assemblages of logic gates that can provide a variety of functions. One day set yourself the exercise of designing an assemblage of gates that can perform the AND, NAND, OR, NOR and XOR functions, depending on the status of control inputs.

Now take that a stage further. Extend that circuit so that it can also add, subtract, divide-by-two, multiply-by-two and so on. And multiply it by eight so that it performs these operations not on one bit at a time, but on 8-bit numbers, ie, numbers which can be expressed in binary code using eight digits, viz decimal numbers between 0 and 255. Clearly you now have a sort of universal logic/arithmetic unit. The trouble is that it will be a comparatively costly unit and you might need a large number of them to perform complex logical operations. It would be cheaper to use discrete gates in a dedicated circuit.

But what you *can* do is this — instead of using large numbers of these multi-purpose units simultaneously switching the data flowing around a complex logic circuit, you use just one of them together with a huge bank of bistables to act as memories. The central processor performs one operation at a time, stores the results for future reference and then proceeds to the next operation which may draw upon those previously stored results and process them further. Clearly there are two quite distinct memory needs: firstly, storage of the input and output data processed by the device and secondly, storage of the sequence of control instructions which tell the processor what operation it must perform next.

And this is just what a microcomputer is. The central processor is called the *microprocessor*. It is, if you like, the 'computer within the computer'. The other essential feature of a microcomputer is a massive bank of memory to store both data and the series of instructions, the 'program' which the computer is to execute (run). And in a home computer we also find a number of *interfaces* by which it is possible for the machine to communicate with the outside world. These include the keyboard by which the operator can enter instructions and data, mass storage interfaces enabling programs and data to be stored on cassette tape, floppy disc or floppy tape (microdrive), interfaces for a monitor (which may be a domestic TV receiver) and normally some means of communicating with the outside world by making sounds.

We shall now look at each of these parts of the microcomputer in turn.

The microprocessor and programming languages

The microprocessor is the heart of the microcomputer that actually does the data processing: in a sense all else is ancillary to it. A microprocessor is a single but complex integrated circuit having the ability to work through a series of instructions and in response to them perform simple logical and arithmetical operations on numbers. We shall confine our comments to the simpler 8-bit microprocessors as used in the BBC Micro and Sinclair Spectrum. There are other microprocessors which can handle 16-bit and 32-bit numbers and so are faster and more versatile.

The operations which the microprocessor can handle are in fact very limited. They include the ability to add, subtract and compare 8-bit numbers, multiply or divide them by two, AND them, OR them and exclusive-OR them. It can copy the contents of any memory location into its own internal registers (its own 8-bit memories which it uses for its operations), can transfer them between registers and back to any memory location. It can jump to another part of memory and execute the instructions it finds there (like a BASIC 'GOTO') and it can jump to a subroutine elsewhere in memory and execute that before returning to the next instruction in the original sequence (like a BASIC 'GOSUB').

Since it is only capable of these fairly simple operations you may wonder how the computer is able to perform complex calculations such as:

PRINT 12345 * 6.789

and present the answer apparently instantaneously. The answer is that the microprocessor would of necessity break that single BASIC statement into a large number of smaller, simpler operations that it *can* manage in much the same way that you or I, if we were called upon to work it out without the aid of a machine, would break it down into the succession of simple multiplications and additions that we call 'long multiplication'. Each operation on the microprocessor might take on average 4 or 5 microseconds so that even if a thousand such operations were necessary the whole process would take only 4 or 5 milliseconds, less than the time between frames on your monitor screen. So the whole complex process appears to happen instantaneously and the computer tricks you into thinking that it finds floating-point decimal arithmetic the most natural thing in the world.

Not surprisingly, then, it comes as a shock to some home computer users to find that the BASIC in which they program their machines is in fact an alien environment to the microprocessor itself. The microprocessor does not understand BASIC — it only understands that limited range of instructions (just 56 of them in the 6502 microprocessor used by the BBC Micro) generally called *machine code*. Even when your computer is running a BASIC program, the microprocessor regards itself as running a machine-code program — BASIC is itself a machine-code program and so-called BASIC programs are perhaps more accurately termed 'BASIC applications'. Using a piece of machine code called the 'BASIC interpreter' the microprocessor scans through a BASIC instruction and looks up the keywords and symbols in a table which refers it to further machine-code routines enabling it to implement the application specified in the BASIC instruction.

Why, then, do we program home computers in such 'foreign' languages as BASIC? Why not program them directly in machine code? The answer is that you can do just that if you wish, but it's terribly tedious. BASIC has the virtue of being usually fairly intelligible, even to the novice programmer (indeed BASIC is the acronym for *Beginners' All-Purpose Symbolic Instruction Code*). It's not difficult for anyone the guess what will happen when the computer executes BASIC statements such as:

```
PRINT "Hallo"
```

or,

```
IF X = Y THEN PRINT "Correct!"
```

or even,

```
INPUT "Enter your name ";N$
```

whereas it is not at all obvious what will happen if you poke a few bytes into successive memory locations and command the computer to execute them as machine code.

A further advantage of BASIC is that if you make a mistake in your program the computer will usually give you an informative error message such as:

```
Variable not found at 140:1
```

or,

```
Mistake at line 220
```

Machine code, in contrast, gives no such error messages. Usually the computer just 'hangs up'. The disadvantage of BASIC is that, despite appearances, it is slow. If you take a simple program such as:

```
10 FOR X = 33 TO 126
20 PRINT CHR$X;
30 NEXT X
```

the loop will be executed 94 times and on each of those 'passes' each statement will be interpreted afresh into machine code, the microprocessor repeating largely the same operations. The same effect could be implemented in 6502 machine code (on the BBC Micro/Acorn Electron) as follows:

```
1962 A2 21    LDX #33
1964 8A       .loop TXA
1965 20 EE FF JSR &FFEE
1968 E8       INX
1969 E0 7F    CPX #127
196B D0 F7    BNE loop
196D 60       RTS

>CALL&1962

!"#$%& '( )*+ ,- ./0123456789 : ;<=>?@ABCDEFGHIJKLMNOPQRSTUVWXYZ[ \ ]
^_£abcdefghijklmnopqrstuvwxyz{ | }~>
```

(For the benefit of those not initiated into the mysteries of machine code the above listing is made up as follows. The left column gives in hexadecimal the numbers of the memory locations where the code is located. The second (and third and fourth columns where used) give the hexadecimal contents of the memory. The fifth and sixth columns give a 'mnemonic' describing the operation and the argument (generally called the *operand*) which determines how the operation is used. Thus LDX means 'LoaD the X register', TXA means 'Transfer the contents of the X register to the A register', JSR means 'Jump to the SubRoutine at. . .' and so on.)

The principal advantage of machine code is its speed of execution, since there is no need for time-consuming interpretation. Fast-action arcade-style games generally *have* to be in machine code since BASIC cannot manipulate the data fast enough. For many other applications, however, BASIC has adequate speed and this is true of most of the applications considered in this book.

A second advantage of machine code is that it is miserly in its use of memory. The simple machine-code program listed above occupies only 12 bytes of memory and needs no space for variables. The BASIC program that it replaced occupies 29 bytes in BBC BASIC even with all spaces omitted and would also need space for the variable X. It's not always true, however, that machine code implementations are shorter than BASIC ones. The machine code to multiply 12345 by 6.789 would be very cumbersome and would take far more space than the corresponding BASIC instruction.

BASIC, as we have seen, bears very little resemblance to the machine code into which it is interpreted. For this reason it is called a 'high-level language'. There are, as we shall see, 'low-level languages' which have a much closer similarity to machine code. There are, however, other high-level languages which combine convenience with greater speed than BASIC. Two examples are FORTH and PASCAL. These overcome the time-consuming interpretation by *compiling* their machine code (or something close to it) before execution. So, as soon as you have finished keying in your FORTH program the compiler converts it to an intermediate code that is stored in memory and requires minimal interpretation. When you run the program it is the compiled code, not what you keyed in, that is run.

Those without the motivation to learn or the means to acquire other high-level languages who need the speed of machine code or who wish to learn more about the inner workings of the microprocessor can use a *low-level* compiling language such as Assembly Language. An *assembler* is a program which compiles machine code from easily remembered mnemonic codes such as those that we met in the earlier machine-code listing. BBC/Electron users are well catered for in that BBC BASIC incorporates a very versatile assembler permitting Assembly language to be incorporated into BASIC programs. Indeed an example of this can be seen in the progressive cab control project (Chapter 5). The Spectrum does not include an assembler, but several excellent Z-80 assemblers for the Spectrum are available commercially.

Memory — ROM and RAM
The second essential requirement of a microcomputer is *memory*. This is needed both for the storage of the program being executed and for the storage of data associated with the program — including *screen memory*, ie, the computer must remember the pattern of dots (pixels) that makes up the current monitor display.

Two types of memory can be found in each home computer: *read-only memory* (ROM) and *read/write memory* more usually called *random-access memory* (RAM). This designation is misleading, however, since the random-access capability is just as applicable to ROM as it is to RAM.

ROM, as its name suggests, is memory that cannot be altered by the computer. The computer can read the data or execute the programs stored in it but cannot alter it. If you write a program to poke a new value into a byte of ROM the program will appear to run normally but subsequent checking of the value stored in that byte will reveal that it still contains its original value; your attempt to poke a new value has had no effect.

So what is the use of ROM? ROM is used to store those programs and data that the microcomputer needs all the while simply to *be* a microcomputer. The BASIC interpreter, for instance, will normally be stored in ROM. (An exception is the Tatung Einstein in which BASIC must be loaded from disc into RAM.) Also in ROM will be a host of machine-code routines concerned with the machine's built-in interfaces, eg, routines concerned with getting data from the keyboard, displaying characters and graphics on the screen, and loading and saving programs and data on the mass storage system. These routines are independent of BASIC in the sense that they will also be used by other languages such as FORTH or by utilities such as word processors which may be loaded into RAM or may be present in other ROM ics.

One of the fundamental differences between the BBC Micro and the Spectrum is that in the BBC there is a sharp distinction between BASIC which occupies one 16Kbyte ROM chip and the interface routines which are generally called the machine *operating system* (OS); this occupies another 16Kbyte ROM chip. On the BBC both ROMS have their own commands, OS commands being distinguished by beginning with a '★'. The currently active language automatically passes any command beginning with a '★' to the OS's command line interpreter (OSCLI). In the Spectrum there is no hard distinction between the BASIC interpreter and the OS which share the same 16Kbyte ROM.

RAM is generally taken to mean that part of the computer's random-access memory that is available to the user to store his programs and data. One of the many sales points of home computers has centred around the amount of RAM available and a part of the perpetual debate between Spectrum (48K) and BBC (32K) owners is that the Spectrum's extra 16K of RAM gives it superiority. That, however, is a shortsighted argument. ROM can be as important as RAM since extra routines in ROM can make user programs shorter, saving RAM. Adding ROM to RAM both machines have 64K, as has the Commodore 64, claimed as the world's best selling home computer.

This recurrence of the number 64K (in fact 65536) as the total number of bytes of memory is no coincidence. Let's go back and look at the microprocessor again. As previously mentioned it contains a number of eight-bit registers capable of holding numbers between 0 and 255 (a total of 256 different possibilities). Obviously the microprocessor has registers used especially for addressing memory for reading or writing purposes. If the memory address register were a simple 8-bit register we should obviously be limited to a mere 256 bytes of memory which would make for a microcomputer of such limited capability as to be of no practical use.

To make a practical machine the addressing system uses a 16-bit register (in effect a pair of 8-bit registers) which gives the possibility of addressing 256 × 256 = 65536 (or 64K) memory locations. For this reason *every 8-bit microprocessor reckons itself to be working in a 64K of memory environment.* That 64K will be made up partly of ROM and partly of RAM. It may not all be present — the earlier 16K Spectrums and 16K BBCs have 'gaps' in the memory map. Any data stored in a non-existent location will be lost and any attempt to read a non-existent location will yield 255. Even on machines fitted with more than 64K of combined ROM and RAM the microprocessor must regard itself as working with 64K bytes — banks of extra ROM and RAM can be 'paged' in and out even within programs so that a microprocessor might have access to 256K bytes or more, but only ever to 64K of it at a time.

The way in which the 64K is organized varies considerably from machine to machine — indeed the BBC and the Spectrum are 'upside down' with respect to each other. The BBC has its 32K of RAM from &0000 to &7FFF and its ROM from &8000 to &FFFF — BASIC from &8000 to &BFFF and OS from &C000 to &FFFF (actually it's not as simple as that since &FFC0 to &FEFF is RAM set apart for the so-called 'memory-mapped peripherals'). The Spectrum has its BASIC/OS from &0000 to &3FFF (actually ROM finishes a little below this, there being a few hundred bytes 'gap' just below &3FFF) and its RAM from &4000 to &FFFF.

The interfaces

A microcomputer that consisted simply of a microprocessor and memory would be a singularly useless piece of equipment because there would be no means by which programs or data could be fed into it and no way in which the data it had processed could be made available to the outside world. Consequently a third requirement of any microcomputer is sufficient interfacing to enable it to fulfil its purpose. On a home computer the bare essentials are a keyboard for the manual entry of programs and data, a mass storage interface, typically cassette tape, so that programs and data can be saved and reloaded, a UHF modulator allowing a domestic TV receiver to be used as a monitor for the display of text and graphics and a sound generator so that music or sound effects can be added to make programs more interesting. Both the BBC and the Spectrum offer these interfaces as standard. Both machines also offer access to the main data busses so that other equipment can be connected and addressed as though part of the machine's memory. The BBC Model B also has as standard an analogue input port, an 8-bit user port, a serial communications port, a parallel printer port and a disc drive connection (though this only becomes active when an optional disc interface and disc filing system is fitted).

All these interfaces are essentially similar in-so-far as they allow the microprocessor to receive data from the outside world or to send data to the outside world. No matter what form those data take in the outside world to the microprocessor they are 8-bit bytes or groups of bytes or parts of bytes. Moreover, the microprocessor, just as it does not understand BASIC, similarly does not know what an interface is. A routine which we know activates an interface is, so far as the microprocessor is concerned, just another poke to a certain memory location or just another machine code subroutine. Thus on the BBC Micro sending data via the user port is simply poking data into location &FE60 (having first of all configured the port as an output) or putting a '1' on the screen is simply execution of the machine code at &FFEE with 49 (the ASCII code for '1') in the microprocessor's A register.

Conclusion

Microcomputers may, as we said at the outset of this survey, have an aura of mystique about them, but when considered part-by-part are essentially simple machines. They are not 'electronic brains' as their forbears were dubbed in the '50s. They are not even particularly clever. Their importance stems from their ability to perform simple operations very fast. The programmer's art consists in taking real-life tasks and breaking them down into simple operations which the microprocessor can emulate and perform more quickly and more accurately than the human brain.

Anyone who has ever seriously 'played' with a home computer will know how 'stupid' it can be — it always does just what we tell it (assuming that it is a practical operation) and not what any human being would know we *intended* to tell it to do. And who has

not found himself shouting at his computer, 'What do you mean —
''no such variable at line 200'' — I defined that variable in line 150!'
forgetting that either line 200 could be executed before line 150 or
that some intermediate operation might wipe out the portion of
RAM where the offending variable is stored.

Whatever may be the value of microcomputers for performing
practical applications in model railways or any other field of human
endeavour their use remains unrivalled as an exercise in clarity of
thought and personal humility — for be sure that your programming errors will find you out!

Appendix 3

The BBC Micro's user port

Physical properties

Physically the BBC Micro's user port is one of the array of connectors on the front of the machine's printed circuit board and best seen by tilting the front of the machine upwards and peering beneath the keyboard. The socket itself is as shown in Figure A3.1 — please note that this diagram is correct — that given in the 3rd edition of the *Advanced User Guide for the BBC Micro* is wrong.

To make your connection to the socket you will need a 20-pin insulation-displacement header and a length of 20-way ribbon cable (or two lengths of 10-way ribbon cable). Before you baulk at the prospect of making 20 ultra-subminiature soldered connections in the header, let me assure you that no soldering is necessary. You may need to trim the ribbon cable's end square first and if the conductors are more closely spaced than the serrations in the header it helps to cut between them with a modelling knife and spread them a little. Then you merely insert the end of the ribbon cable into the

Figure A3.1 BBC Micro User Port as seen from the front.

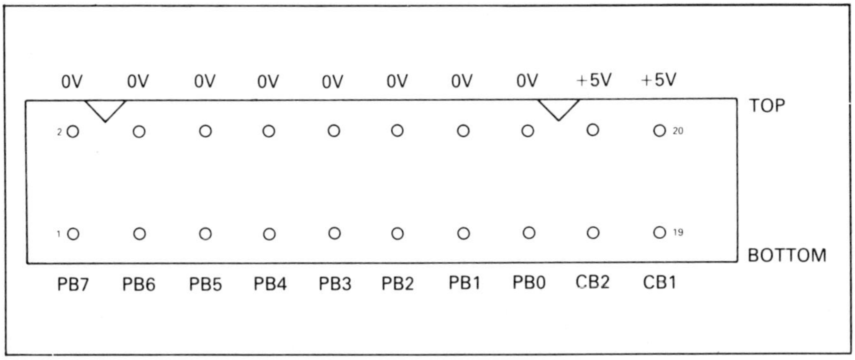

slot and push the rear part of the header into the main body until it clicks. Sharp metallic teeth inside the header penetrate the insulation and make electrical connection. Pins 1 and 20 connect to the wires at the edge of the cable.

Even numbered pins 0 to 16 are internally connected in parallel to the machine's ground line. The two +5V lines (pins 18 and 20) are connected in parallel and can be used to power a limited amount of external circuitry.

Electrical properties

The user port is one of the facilities generally known as the *memory-mapped peripherals*. That is to say, it occupies a place in the machine's memory. But its behaviour is a little different from ordinary bytes of memory.

Simplest to understand are the eight pins labelled PB0 to PB7. These represent the eight bits of the user port byte which is &FE60. But just as a byte of RAM can be written to (poked) or read from (peeked), so the user port can be used for sending data (ie, as an output register) or for receiving data (ie, as an input register) but it has to be programmed first. Each of the eight bits can be separately programmed to behave as a data sender or receiver. This is done by poking an eight-bit binary number into the *data direction register* whose address is &FE62. The number is calculated by writing a '1' for each bit required as an output and a '0' for each bit required as an input. Thus to use all eight bits as inputs you would need to issue ?&FE62=0; for all eight bits as outputs ?&FE62=&FF; for bit 7 as input and the remainder as outputs ?&FE62=8F.

Inputs and outputs to the port bits are standard TTL with pull-up resistors allowing easy interfacing with other logic circuitry. In addition to these eight port bits, the User Port offers a pair of 'control bits' CB1 and CB2. These can be used in a variety of ways and significantly enhance the versatility of the user port. For instance, they can be used as interrupt input and handshake output when transferring data to another device, though that is unlikely to be much use in model railway applications. The operations performed by CB1 and CB2 are determined by the four most significant bits of the *peripheral control register*(pcr), &FE6C.

CB1 can only be used as an interrupt control. That is to say, when activated it simply inhibits the microprocessor's operation and forces the computer to wait until the interrupt has disappeared. The most obvious example of this is seen when using a printer to print out text files or program listings: the computer can send the data much faster than the printer can print them so on the screen you see the data being printed in 'spurts' as it is sent to the printer. When the printer's internal buffer is full it sends an interrupt signal to the computer which means 'Wait! I've no room for any more at present'. So the computer is forced to wait while the printer processes the data in its buffer. When the number of bytes remaining to be processed falls to a certain critical level the interrupt signal is removed and there is another rush of data from the computer to the printer (and screen). Bit 4 of the pcr determines the polarity of the interrupt signal on CB1; if bit 4 is a '0' a '0' on CB1 forces an interrupt; if a '1' then a '1' on CB1 forces an interrupt.

CB2 is more versatile, bits 5 to 7 of the pcr determining its action. If bit 7 is a '1' CB2 becomes an output. With bits 5 and 6 both low it offers a 'handshake output'. Again, this is best illustrated by analogy with the printer port, which is a mirror image of the user port, being the other half of the same 6522 Versatile Interface Adapter (VIA). The data sent to the printer consists mostly of the ASCII codes of characters, 8-bit numbers. It takes the computer a brief but nevertheless finite time to set up the eight bits on the eight separate outputs of the printer port. It is therefore essential that the printer should not 'accept' the byte until the computer has finished setting it up. So the printer waits until it receives a 'handshake' signal from the computer: this is only sent when the computer has set up the required data. When the printer receives the 'handshake' it transfers the byte to the next available space in its buffer and signals the computer by — you've guessed it — sending an interrupt signal on the other control line. This interrupt, however is only a temporary one of a few microseconds. It does, however, force the computer to clear its handshake signal and, when the interrupt is cleared, it prepares the next byte to send to the printer. As a handshake output CB2 goes low when data are ready to be read from the output register and is reset by an interrupt request on CB1.

With bit 5 of the pcr high and bit 6 low CB2 functions in much the same way as when 'handshaking' except that its output consists of a brief (1 microsecond) pulse when data are ready to be read from the output register.

When bit 6 of the pcr is high CB2 gives a steady output at the same level as bit 5 of the pcr. Thus to make CB2 permanently high bits 5, 6 and 7 should be all '1's and to make it permanently low pcr bits 5, 6 and 7 should be a '1', a '1' and a '0' respectively. This facility is useful, it being put to excellent use in the progressive cab control project (Chapter 5).

With bit 7 of the pcr a '0' CB2 becomes an input. When bit 5 is a '1' it becomes another interrupt input like CB1 but acting quite independently, the active level being that set on pcr bit 6. With bit 5 a '1' CB2 becomes simply an 'input' whose active level is the current setting of pcr bit 6. How in practice one could use this facility to read a peripheral device is unclear.

The 6522 VIA is a very versatile chip and has many more facilities but their use is a specialised art. For instance, it contains several timers operating at 1MHz which make possible the use of the BBC Micro for pulse-width modulation applications. This kind of application demands the use of machine code, BASIC being far too slow. A succession of attempts to develop a PWM controller using these facilities, however, was totally unsuccessful. Attempts to find someone who had developed a successful program of this sort similarly failed until within a week of the copy deadline for this book, but unfortunately his filed copy of the program had been lost! Readers with a lot of time and patience, a good knowledge of 6502 Assembly Language programming and an even better grasp of Chapter 22 of the *Advanced User Guide for the BBC Micro* may eventually be able to make use of this remarkable facility.

Index